EDITORS

David Elms and David Wilkinson are both Professors of Civil Engineering
at the University of Canterbury, Christchurch, New Zealand.

COVER PHOTOGRAPH — THE BRIDGE TO NOWHERE

This picture symbolises the importance of sustainable management of the environment. The Mangapurua settlement was a remote farming area in the Mangapurua Valley, now in the Whanganui National Park, North Island, New Zealand. It was established as a rehabilitation scheme to reward returning servicemen from the First World War. Road access from Raetihi was marginal so the most preferred supply route for the settlers was the river boat fleet which plied the Whanganui River.

The bush clad hills were enthusiastically cleared by the settlers and stock introduced but, almost from the start, the writing was on the wall for this and other nearby settlements due to unsustainable land management practices. The settlement was abandoned just before World War II.

The Bridge to Nowhere was constructed in an effort to improve road access to the settlement and spans the Mangapurua Stream where it is now a principal attraction in the National Park. Only a handful of vehicles ever used the bridge and the land then reverted to bush, leaving the bridge in splendid isolation. The old abandoned road provides excellent walking tracks giving access to the bridge, which is also not far from the upper reaches of the Whanganui River.

The Environmentally Educated Engineer

FOCUS ON FUNDAMENTALS

Proceedings of a Workshop on the Fundamentals of Environmental
Engineering Education held at the University of Canterbury,
Christchurch, New Zealand, 22-24 August 1994

David Elms and David Wilkinson
Editors

**Centre for Advanced Engineering
University of Canterbury**
March 1995

ISBN 0-908993-08-0

First Published March 1995

Copyright

© 1995 Centre for Advanced Engineering, University of Canterbury, Private Bag 4800, Christchurch, New Zealand.

Cover

Cover Design by Ken Hudson Graphics, Christchurch.
Photograph: "The Bridge to Nowhere" courtesy of the Conservation Design Centre, Department of Conservation.

Printing

Piranha Print Ltd, Christchurch.

Editorial Services and Book Design

Charles Hendtlass and Janine Griffin, Centre for Advanced Engineering.

Disclaimer

It will be noted that the authorship of this document has been attributed to the many individuals and organisations who have been involved in its production. While all sections have been subject to review and final editing, the opinions expressed remain those of the authors responsible and do not necessarily reflect the views of the Centre for Advanced Engineering.

CONTENTS

Acknowledgements   iii

Abbreviations   v

General Introduction and Overview David Elms   1

Keynote Addresses

The Fundamentals of Environmental Engineering Roger Blakeley   11

Why We are Here David Elms   15

**The Need for Environmental Engineering Education
Fundamentals** David Thom   25

Sustainable Development, Engineering Education and Activity
Roger Duffel   37

Environmental Engineering Education: Turn to Face the Sun
Gary Codner   53

Sustainable Development and Technology Jennifer DuBose,
J David Frost, Jean-Lou A Chameau and Jorge A Vanegas   73

Continuing Engineering Education Sirkka Pöyry   87

General Papers

**Course Design in Environmental Engineering: The Advantage
of Hindsight** David L Wilkinson   99

**Training Environmental Engineers at Tertiary Level: An
Asia-Pacific Perspective** John E Hay   105

**From Reductionist to Systems Thinking: The Engineering
Imperative** John St J S Buckeridge   119

The Fundamentals of Environmental Engineering Education
Marino M Mena   125

**Artifactual Engineering as a Fundamental of Environmental
Engineering** Naomasa Nakajima and Hiroyuki Yoshikawa   129

Regional Papers

**Foundations of Environmental Engineering Education in Negara
Brunei Darussalam** Mirhassan Abu Bakar and Terence Mansfield   135

Environmental Education in China Jiang Zhanpeng   141

Environmental Engineering Education in Indonesia
A H Djajadiningrat   149

**Environmental Engineering Education in Major Japanese
National Universities** N Tambo   155

Environmental Engineering Education in Malaysia
M A Hashim   165

**Developments in Environmental Engineering Education in
Papua New Guinea** G K N S Subasinghe and S Bordia   171

Environmental Engineering Education in Singapore
L C C Koe   179

**Environmental Engineering Education — the Thailand
Experience** Wongpun Limpaseni   185

**The Fundamentals of Environmental Engineering Education
in Vietnam** Pham Ngoc Dang   189

Appendix 1: Group Sessions   193

Appendix 2: Workshop Participants   201

Appendix 3: Biographies of Keynote Speakers   205

Acknowledgements

Sponsoring Organisations

 United Nations Educational, Scientific and Cultural Organisation

 The Association for Engineering Education in Southeast Asia and the Pacific

 World Federation of Engineering Organizations

IACEE   International Association for Continuing Engineering Education

 Centre for Advanced Engineering

Contributing Organisations

 Ministry for the Environment

 Institution of Professional Engineers New Zealand

 University of Canterbury

Thanks also to UNEP, IEAust and the many other organisations and institutions that contributed materially to the success of the Workshop by sending representatives.

Members of the Steering/Advisory Committee for the Workshop:

- Roger Blakeley, Secretary for the Environment, Past Chairman, OECD Environment Committee
- John Buckeridge, Head of Civil and Environmental Engineering, UNITEC Institute of Technology, Auckland
- David Elms, University of Canterbury
- Ian Gunn, University of Auckland
- Bob Hill, Chairman, IPENZ Engineering and Environment Committee
- Mark Milke, University of Canterbury
- David Painter, Lincoln University
- John Peet, University of Canterbury
- Ian Robertson, Royds Consulting, Dunedin
- David Thom, Chairman, WFEO Committee on Engineering and the Environment
- David Wilkinson, University of New South Wales, Australia

Members of the Workshop Organising Committee:

- John Blakeley, Centre for Advanced Engineering
- David Elms, University of Canterbury
- Mark Milke, University of Canterbury
- John Peet, University of Canterbury
- Cliff Stevenson, Centre for Advanced Engineering

Members of the Editorial Staff:

- Janine Griffin, Centre for Advanced Engineering
- Charles Hendtlass, Centre for Advanced Engineering

Members of the Rapporteur Team:

Chairman	Professor David Wilkinson, Department of Civil Engineering, University of Canterbury (formerly School of Civil Engineering, University of New South Wales, Australia)
Members	Dr John Buckeridge, Head of Civil and Environmental Engineering, UNITEC Institute of Technology, Auckland
	Dr Mark Milke, Department of Civil Engineering, University of Canterbury
	Dr John Peet, Department of Chemical and Process Engineering, University of Canterbury

Abbreviations

AAES	American Association of Engineering Societies
AEESEAP	The Association for Engineering Education in Southeast Asia and the Pacific
AIWPS	advanced integrated wastewater pond system
APACE	Appropriate Technology and Community Environment
ASEAN	Association of South East Asian Nations
ASPEI	Association of South Pacific Environmental Institutions
BATNEEC	best available technology not entailing excessive cost
BPEO	best practicable environmental option
BRE	Building Research Establishment
BSRIA	Building Services Research and Information Association
C3P2	Conservation, Compliance, Cleanup and Pollution Prevention
CACA	Chartered Association of Certified Accountants
CAL	Computer-aided Learning
CDP	Committee of Directors in Polytechnics (UK)
CEE	Continuing Engineering Education
CEng	Certificate in Engineering
CEP	Catalytic Extraction Processing
CET	Continuing Education and Training Programme
CIESIN	Consortium for International Earth Science Information Network
CIRIA	Construction Industry Research and Information Association
COMETT	Community Programme for Education and Training in Technology
DEC	Department of Environment and Conservation
DEE	Department of Environmental Engineering
DICE	Database of Information on Continuing Engineering Education
DOD	Department of Defense
DOE	Division of Environment
EA	environmental audit
EC/UK	Engineering Council of the United Kingdom
EIA	Environmental Impact Assessment
ENSEARCH	Environmental Management and Research Association of Malaysia

ENTREE	Environmental Training in Engineering Education
EPEA	European Polytechnic Environmental Association
EPEA	European Polytechnic Environmental Association
FASK	Framework, Attitude, Skills and Knowledge
FEANI	European Federation of National Engineering Associations
FEISEAP	Federation of Engineering Organisations of Southeast Asia and the Pacific
FIDIC	International Association of Consulting Engineers
GNP	Gross National Product
IACEE	International Association for Continuing Engineering Education
ICC	International Chamber of Commerce
ICE	Institution of Civil Engineers
IChemE	Institution of Chemical Engineers
IEAust	Institution of Engineers, Australia
IEng	Institution of Engineers
IMunE	Institution of Municipal Engineers
INTAN	National Institute of Public Administration
IPENZ	Institution of Professional Engineers New Zealand
IRDAC	Industrial Research and Advisory Committee of the European Commission
IStructE	Institution of Structural Engineers
ITB	Institut Teknologi Brunei [Brunei Darussalam]
ITB	Institute of Technology Bandung [Indonesia]
ITN-ITB	International Training Network — Bandung Institute of Technology Centre
JBM	Joint Board of Moderation
MEM	Master of Environmental Management
NCE	National Council for the Environment
NGO	Non-governmental organisation
OEC	Office of the Environment and Conservation
PCFC	Polytechnics and Colleges Funding Council (UK)
PERPAMSI	Indonesian Waterworks Association
PHE	Public Health Engineering

PNGUT	Papua New Guinea University of Technology
RACE	Research into Artifacts Centre for Engineering
RIAScot	Royal Incorporation of Architects in Scotland
RTPI	Royal Town Planning Institute
SEFI	European Society for Engineering Education
SERC	Science and Engineering Council (UK)
SMEs	small and medium-sized enterprises
SPREP	South Pacific Regional Environmental Programme
TEK	Finnish Association of Graduate Engineers
TELI	Tufts Environmental Literacy Institute
TH-Delft	Technical High School of Delft
UATI	International Union of Technical Associations
UETP	University Enterprise Training Programme
UETP-EEE	University Enterprise Training Programme in Environmental Engineering Education
UKM	National University of Malaysia
UNCED	United Nations Conference on Environment and Development
UNDP	United Nations Development Programme
UNEP	United Nations Environment Programme
UNESCO	United Nations Educational, Scientific and Cultural Organisation
UPNG	University of Papua New Guinea
USEPA	United States Environmental Protection Agency
USM	University of Science Malaysia
WEPSD	World Engineering Partnership for Sustainable Development
WEPSD	World Engineering Partnership for Sustainable Development
WFEO	World Federation of Engineering Organisations
WHO	World Health Organisation

General Introduction and Overview

David Elms

This book is the record of a four-day international workshop at which 37 invited participants discussed the foundations on which the education of environmentally-involved engineers should ideally be built. A great deal of hard thinking went into the matter. Despite participants having different backgrounds, the workshop ended with a very strong measure of agreement on some key issues, particularly that a significant number, perhaps a quarter, of all engineers need a broader and more systems-oriented training than that which is currently the norm.

The first ideas for the workshop arose from discussions between David Thom and myself in October 1993. We talked about the growing imperative for engineers to be environmentally aware and of the need to respond to the demands of societies throughout the world for greater environmental sensitivity. Technology had to be environmentally appropriate as the movement towards the sustainable management of resources increased its momentum. Clearly, more emphasis had to be put on the environmental education of engineers and engineering students.

The more we talked, the more we came to believe that adding environmental courses to existing engineering curricula would not be enough. A deeper level of change was needed. Indeed, what we seemed to be looking for was a rather different sort of engineer, one who would be broader-based and with skills significantly different from those of most conventional engineers.

At that stage, it was not something we were able to articulate in any detail, certainly not to the extent of being able to draw up a specification of the sort of person, the sort of skills and knowledge, that we were talking about. Rather, we simply felt that the new type of engineer would, in some sense, be fundamentally different, though we did not at that stage see how.

The education of such an engineer would have to be fundamentally different as well. It would not just be a matter of adding a few extra courses to the existing curriculum. What seemed to be needed was a fundamentally different thrust, starting right from the beginning with the initial messages being given to the students from the very first as to what engineering was about. This seemed important, as it is the initial, early-level courses that give the thrust and direction to the rest of an engineer's education.

We did not mean to imply that there was anything wrong with the content of engineering education as it is currently taught. A rigorous training in engineering technique, giving analytic and design capability and an ability to deal quantitatively with technical matters in a thoroughly disciplined way is necessary for all engineers and is as important nowadays as it ever was. It was not a question of objecting to the existing content. Rather, it was a matter of completeness, of balance, that some things which seemed important for the new engineer we were thinking of were either downplayed or wholly absent. To begin with, there was the matter of complexity, of the behaviour of complex systems, which is increasingly coming to be recognised as a discipline in its own right. It is important in the training of an environmentally-educated engineer, as the problems at the meeting place of technical matters with both the natural and the social environment are often exceedingly complex. Complexity is also a characteristic of management, of matters involving safety and risk, and of many other aspects of professional engineering. Yet virtually all the early-level training of the professional engineer deals with simple physical models. It is not to say the problems involved are not hard, or that training is not demanding or rigorous. They are — but the models are not complex.

Neither was complexity the only element missing. Subjects such as communication, ethics and creativity were generally absent or inadequately covered.

It seemed to us that around the world there was a great deal of talk about environmental engineering education, but very little about its foundations, about the fundamental early-level courses that give students the direction and motivation on which they build the rest of their studies. Yet it is the foundations that arguably have most influence on the attitudes with which students emerge at the end of their university training. More specialised and specific courses can give particular skills as well as the body of knowledge that education must impart, but skills and knowledge are not enough. Even more important is the framework within which they are used, which is very much governed by the attitude, by the world view, the *weltanschauung*, of the student. And so, where environmental engineering and environmental awareness are introduced by adding new courses at a later stage to what is basically an older and unchanged curriculum framework, the results will be new knowledge, but unchanged attitudes.

As these ideas grew within us, we came increasingly to feel there was a need for a forum to discuss such matters. Thus began the idea of the workshop. It had to be a workshop — a conference is no place for the concentrated discussion the subject needed. So we decided to invite key figures, primarily from the Southeast Asia/Pacific region (AEESEAP's area of interest), but also from further afield where we thought helpful contributions could be made.

As the idea grew, so too did encouragement as others agreed with the importance of the issues and put their weight behind the proposal in various ways. Though the initial thinking came from AEESEAP and the WFEO Committee on Engineering and the Environment, we were soon joined by UNESCO, the Centre for Advanced Engineering (CAE), the IACEE and the New Zealand Ministry for the Environment, while many other organisations, such as UNEP, IPENZ, IEAust and the Japan Society for Engineering Education, contributed by sending delegates. The degree of support was heartening and reinforced our belief that we were dealing with both an important and a timely issue.

The workshop itself was in four parts or cycles, each building on the one before. The first addressed the needs of industry and the profession — what were the sorts of jobs the environmental engineer would be required to do? The second cycle looked at the framework, attitude, skills and knowledge (FASK) needed for addressing the tasks identified in the first round. Next came the question of the teaching implications for providing the identified FASK components, particularly focusing on the early-level foundation teaching required. Finally, the fourth cycle addressed continuing engineering education and the implications for the professional development of engineers in practice.

Each cycle began with a keynote contribution, an address designed to set the direction and outline the issues for the subsequent discussions. This was followed by small group discussions at some length. Finally, the thinking of the groups was considered by the whole workshop in a plenary session. A four-person editorial team led by David Wilkinson had the task of organising the results of the discussions into a coherent set of decisions and recommendations. (See Appendix 1 for an outline of these discussions.)

From the beginning of the workshop, it was clear that different countries had different needs, so that their educational priorities and attitudes were also different. This was scarcely surprising. However, with the focus of the workshop consistently aiming at fundamentals rather than at details, a strong sense of consensus began to develop, to the extent that at the end there was a feeling of solid agreement on the overall direction engineering education should take. An unusually strong (for such meetings) sense of enthusiasm and energy built up during the course of the workshop as participants began to realise both the appropriateness of the issues and the commonality of the views that were being expressed and developed.

The first task was to agree on the precise focus of the workshop. Was it dealing with the education of environmental engineers or with the environmental education of engineers? It was soon agreed that it was the latter. However, it was still true that two types of engineer were considered at the workshop: the general engineer, and what, for want of a better word, could be called the "environmentally involved engineer". As for the former, it was agreed that all engineers, no matter what their primary discipline, needed to be environmentally educated to the extent that they would need to understand the issues involved in, say, sustainable management and cleaner production. Environmentally involved engineers, on the other hand, would be those dealing with engineering matters that specifically and directly interacted with the natural and social environments. An example would be the design and construction of large projects — dams, for instance — that would have a significant environmental impact. This is in contrast with the more narrow definition of environmental engineer as a modern version of the older sanitary or public health engineer and who is primarily involved in waste disposal and pollution control.

Interestingly, none of the practising engineers attending the workshop called themselves environmental engineers, despite having a high degree of involvement in environmental matters. David Thom, for instance, who has a great wealth of experience with the environment, told us that he regards himself as a civil, not an environmental, engineer.

It seemed that we really needed a new name. As none came to mind, we agreed to proceed using the term "environmentally educated engineer" to mean both the general and the environmentally-involved engineer.

The point was made that in practice, by no means all "environmental engineers" in the narrower sense are environmentally educated, with many persisting in an older and more limited attitude.

The workshop's principal findings are given in Appendix 1 as they were produced at the time. Looking carefully at them, a number of themes emerge. My own interpretation of the main ideas leads to the following major points:

Needs of Our "Customers"

As the environmental problems facing the world become increasingly grave, so the world's communities, who are ultimately our "customers", need increasingly effective actions from engineers. There is a need for engineers to take positions of leadership. In some countries this is achieved, but in most it is not. There are two primary reasons why engineers are not leaders. The first is the poor public perception of engineers. There needs to be a better, a changed, image in the minds of the public. The second problem is that there is not a clear, effective and direct link between engineers and the community. In contrast to, say, the relationship with lawyers and medical practitioners, there is a lack of a direct interface between engineers and the majority of their "customers". That is, links with the community are indirect, through clients and employers. This results in:

- inadequate recognition of engineers by the community; and

- inadequate understanding of the needs of the community by the engineers.

Because of the urgency of the matter, and its pervasiveness, the problems are particularly evident in environmentally-related matters. For both reasons, engineers are unable to be as effective as the community requires and the lack of interaction means that engineers typically lack many of the skills and capabilities required of them. Therefore:

1. *The interaction and communication between engineers and their "customers" needs to improve.*

2. *Engineers must change this public image.*

3. *Additional skills and capabilities are required of engineers.*

The Kinds of Engineer Required

As well as the need for all engineers to be educated in environmental issues, there is also a need for specialist environmental engineering programmes. The specialist approach needs a *generalist* methodology. In other words, there is a need to *specialise* in generality and complexity. It was thought that there is a requirement for a new type of engineer with a greater breadth of knowledge than the traditional engineer, and with additional skills. However, only a proportion of engineers need to be educated in this way — a figure of 25% was suggested — with the rest having a more traditional education. Thus:

4. *All engineers need to be environmentally educated.*

5. *Specialist environmental engineering courses are required.*

6. *A proportion of engineers must be generalists.*

Requirements for the Environmentally-involved Engineer

Particularly because environmental issues are often complex and not always easily quantified, the sorts of capability required of engineers involved in environmental matters are often markedly different from those expected of traditionally educated engineers. Such capabilities could involve understanding and responding to the needs of the natural environment, dealing with the politically-oriented issues involving the social environment and interacting with professionals from many different disciplines, such as scientists, planners, lawyers, bankers and politicians. While such engineers will have a greater breadth, they must also be technically capable.

The additional capabilities required can be summarised by the acronym ASK, standing for Attitude, Skills and Knowledge. All three are necessary. Specifically:

- The *attitude* required has several components. One is an environmental ethic. Another is a holistic approach in which a broad and realistic overview is required, giving a context to specific tasks and actions. A third is a clear vision of system functioning.

- A specific *skill* not commonly taught is an ability to understand and work with complex, interactive and ill-defined systems. Another skill needing emphasis is an ability to work well with people of diverse backgrounds and abilities. Part of this is skill at communication. A high level of creativity is also required as the problems involved are often refractory and particularly difficult to solve.

- A *broad knowledge* of many things is required in addition to a sound technical knowledge. Scientific matters of many kinds must be understood, but there must also be sufficient knowledge of legal issues and social processes. A wide general knowledge is useful too, as it helps creativity.

In addition to these, it is also necessary to have a framework within which the other three components sit. For example, it is not sufficient simply to have knowledge — knowledge of anything. It must be a disciplined body of knowledge acquired for a focused purpose.

In sum, the requirements for environmentally educated and environmentally involved engineers are that they should have:

7. *A holistic approach.*

8. *A clear vision of system functioning.*

9. *Appropriate attitudes, skills and knowledge.*

10. *Systems skills.*

11. *Interaction skills.*

12. *Broad knowledge in specific areas.*

13. *Exposure to significant issues.*

Educational Response — Undergraduate Level

The workshop did not attempt to give detailed specifications for undergraduate courses. Instead, it outlined the necessary attributes of graduates, as summarised in the previous section.

Nevertheless, it was understood throughout that it was never the intention of the workshop to provide detailed course specifications. The aim was always to look at the fundamentals. Initially, this was intended to apply to the early-level courses that set the direction for all that follows. However, the workshop expanded the emphasis to take in a strategic overview of the whole educational endeavour. The central role of early-level teaching was, however, never forgotten throughout these discussions.

Recommendations in this section concentrated on two general areas: firstly, on the essential nature of the proposed courses and, secondly, on implementation issues.

With regard to the nature of the courses, a number of points were made, together with the overall caution that, although the attitude, skills and knowledge required imply a general rather than a narrowly-focused education, nevertheless it is essential that the training should be rigorous and tightly disciplined. Generality does not in the least mean that intellectual discipline can be abandoned. This and other points may be summarised as:

14. *Though courses should aim for generality, they must be intellectually rigorous.*

15. *Courses must have the characteristic of flexibility.*

16. *There is a need to resolve the potential conflict between a tendency to increase specialisation on the one hand and the desire for a common core on the other.*

17. *Priority must be given to problem-based and project-based learning.*

With regard to implementation, there were questions both of priority and of strategic management issues. The overriding management issue that would predominantly determine the successful reception and implementation of any new proposals was identified as the need for senior management support. This would be substantially accomplished in any university agreeing to the Talloires Declaration, which is discussed in Gary Codner's paper.

18. *The first priority in integrating the new ideas within existing course structures is for students to gain understanding of the behaviour of real (complex) systems and how they respond to disturbances.*

19. *Educating the educators must be given priority.*

20. *For integration of programme components, attitudinal issues must be dealt with first, followed by functional issues.*

21. *Significant changes must be driven from the top.*

22. *The educators cannot manage significant change alone — they require help in the form of proactive moves by environmentally sensitive engineers in industry and practice.*

Educational Response — Continuing Engineering Education

The results required of continuing engineering education (CEE) and continuing professional development are similar to those the universities should be producing in their graduates. The specifications outlined above for environmentally-educated engineers are common to the outputs of both. However, needs, issues and means of provision are very different when dealing with professional engineers rather than undergraduates. Of the major points of agreement on CEE issues, first there were two relating to content and nature:

> 23. *There is a need to upskill in concepts of sustainability and environmental law, and to inculcate an environmental ethos.*

> 24. *Quality and sustainability are linked, so quality management and its relationship to sustainability must be emphasised.*

Then came points concerning practical matters, including an emphasis on the roles of and relationship between providers and consumers of CEE. It should be borne in mind that the providers are generally either academics, in-house trainers in large companies and enterprises or independent professional providers. CEE may also be government-driven. The issues raised were:

> 25. *There is a need to focus on both academics (or providers) and practising professionals.*

> 26. *Currently CEE needs are all too often met from the provider's perspective, which is not necessarily that of the practitioner.*

> 27. *Each CEE course or programme will lie on an axis running from the needs of companies on the one hand to the need of individuals for professional enrichment, and the position of the course on this axis determines who initiates it.*

> 28. *There is a need to demonstrate the improvements in efficiency and reduction in cost expected to result from any CEE programme.*

Conclusion

In the end, the workshop achieved almost all we had hoped for. Most of our original questions were answered, and our tentative beliefs were confirmed.

There were two exceptions, though. One was that we did not end up with a clear specification of the ideal environmental or environmentally-involved engineer — the initial focus of the first of the four workshop phases. Perhaps it would have been impossible, given that the workshop pointed up our lack of clarity as to what we meant by environmental engineering. However, what happened was that we realised we were talking about a type of engineer who was more than merely environmentally educated, environmentally aware, but who was very different from the narrowly-defined environmental engineer, that is, an engineer dealing only with public health matters or ventilation and air conditioning. Earlier in this chapter, I used the words "environmentally involved engineer" to describe the type we meant. It was a major achievement of the workshop to develop an understanding of the importance of educating such engineers. The importance, indeed, as much as anything lay in giving them a name, for naming is a precursor of all serious thought. But although it was implied, there was no clear and explicit specification developed of the essential and common nature of the type of work done by environmentally-involved engineers — in other words, of what, at that level, the community requires of engineers.

The second exception was that we had hoped for answers to the question: "On what basic first-level subjects should environmental engineering education be based?" The question was not explicitly addressed. It was implicitly answered to a very large extent, and many of the summary points listed above deal with the issue, but a clear specification must be left to another occasion.

Overall, though given the variety of background of the participants, the degree of unanimity reached and its strength, were remarkable. We were left with a feeling of enthusiasm and of satisfaction that between us, we had achieved a thoroughly useful formulation and clarification of a number of important ideas.

Keynote Addresses

The Fundamentals of Environmental Engineering

Roger Blakeley
Secretary for the Environment
Ministry for the Environment
Wellington, New Zealand

I would like to set the context for the workshop, both regionally and globally. I want to talk about the future shape of engineering environmental education and the dramatic implications for our profession.

I will also address the need to educate all levels of our profession to keep abreast with the changes that lie ahead and conclude with some remarks about innovative environmental technologies.

During the first great wave of environmental concern in the late 1960s and early 1970s, most of the problems seemed local — the products of individual pipes and smokestacks. The answer appeared to lie in regulating these pollution sources.

When the environment re-emerged on the political agenda in the 1980s, the main concerns had become global — acid rain, depletion of the ozone layer and global warming. Analysts sought causes not in pipes and smokestacks, but in the nature of human activities. One report after another concluded that much of what we do, many of our attempts to make "progress", are simply unsustainable.

It is significant that two past presidents of IPENZ — David Thom and the late Murray Sweetman — headed the environment committees of two prestigious international engineering organisations.

Recently, I came across a statement by David Thom that referred to the "strategic plan" for engineering embedded in Agenda 21:

> *"It's not that what we learn of engineering science will be different — but the whole ethos of practice will change. The fundamental basis of practice will be protection of the environment and, where necessary, restoration of natural systems.*
>
> *This will require a review of ethical responsibilities; an education that will produce the facility to think technological options and environmental impacts in a parallel way; an ability to work with multi-disciplinary groups; and a strong social interest."*

That is why tomorrow's crop of engineers must be educated for sustainability. Invariably, they end up working at the leading edge of development and need to have a solid grounding in environmental matters and skills.

Let's face it — the face of engineering is already changing. In the past, engineers built structures to last. Their work was truly monumental, and our cities and towns bear witness to the longevity of many of their structures. Demolition workers tearing down some of these edifices will testify to their solid construction.

But, after that era, we entered the period where the attitude of the day was disposability — it became the throwaway society. Structures were designed not to last a century, but a decade and a half. We thought the world's resources would last forever. Energy was cheap, and it would stay that way.

In my view, the process has to start at the top. We must place a priority on "educating the educators", on the need for sustainability to underpin all engineering thinking. Unless — and until — academics accept this concept fully, it will never be passed on to the students they are teaching.

It has been said that training engineering students on the environment must occur on three different levels: awareness, assessment and immersion.

The first level, awareness, means environmental consciousness-raising for students at both local and global levels. Here, assessment refers to the environmental impact assessment process — integral to the design phase of most engineering works. Immersion takes in the work of the specialised environmental engineer who deals with waste management and so forth.

A standard course for first-year engineering students should address all three needs, including the need for skills in environmental science, social impacts, the world view of indigenous peoples, communication, leadership and ethics.

Those wanting to specialise in non-environmental areas will move on. For others, this will provide foundation skills on which further courses are built.

I understand that at Canterbury University, course instructors have found a common thread in the discipline of the behaviour of complex systems and in the underlying idea that environmental engineering is fundamentally different from traditional engineering. As a result, early-level teaching on the behaviour of complex systems is designed to give the students both understanding and skills in system assessment and formulation.

The Canterbury approach is to train students so that both the extremes found in professionals are avoided — too narrow a technical approach on the one hand and too undisciplined and imprecise a qualitative approach on the other.

The plain truth is that pollution is the most visible sign of inefficiency, waste and short-sighted management. We need only to look at the wholesale poisoning of the land, water and air of Eastern Europe and the former Soviet Union to see what happens when nations industrialise without regard to the environmental costs.

Businesses that reduce waste, conserve energy and cause less pollution tend to be the most profitable and successful in the long term. Business needs to employ good environmental practices because their "bottom line" commercial success will increasingly depend on it.

The term "eco-efficiency" was coined at Rio to describe those businesses that are able to add maximum value with minimum resource use and minimal pollution. Eco-efficiency means making sure that businesses combine the goals of good business management with care for the environment. In the two years since Rio, industry has been discovering the truth of the eco-efficiency message — that factoring in good environmental practices can give it a competitive edge.

I read recently that it is now acknowledged in Japan that the biggest new market in the history of world business is the market for the new products and processes that make it possible to achieve economic progress without environmental destruction. There is a major market opportunity for innovative technology in areas such as wastewater treatment and alternative fuels, and environmental consulting services. Engineers need to get the message that the global environmental technology industry is worth US$200 billion per year and will continue to grow rapidly.

One of the best ways of implementing these policies is by adopting the concept of "cleaner production", which aims to reduce the adverse impact of production and service activities on the environment.

The fundamentals of environmental engineering are:

- the *environment* must be seen as holistic, recognising the interdependence and interaction of people and the natural and physical environment;

- *engineering* must recognise the obligations of the professional engineer to the global community in its widest sense, to the client, employer and colleagues; and

- *engineering education* must give the professional engineers of today and tomorrow broad-based skills in environmental and social sciences, economics, technology, communication, leadership and ethics. It must be a process of continuing professional development and life-long learning.

Professional engineers have the opportunity and challenge to be leaders in creating a better world for the future.

Why We are Here

David Elms
Department of Civil Engineering
University of Canterbury
Christchurch, New Zealand

Introduction

I enjoy ambiguous titles. Thus, the title "Why we are here" deliberately contains a number of meanings. Explore them as you will. The most obvious is that I want to discuss the background to the workshop and its rationale and so explain how it is we are here. But first, a story to underline another meaning. Once, long ago, a young woman sat outside on a window sill far above the ground, full of despair and wanting to jump, yet hesitating. "Well, tell me what there is to live for," she said to me angrily. So I told her. It seemed to be the thing to do. The issue was urgent and important. Happily, she came back into the room.

So too with the workshop. The issues it deals with, and ultimately the reasons for dealing with them, are also urgent and important. We are engaged in more than just an intellectual exercise. This needs to be said first and remembered as part of the background to everything else we do.

Now to the specifics of the workshop and its background. Consider its title, *The Fundamentals of Environmental Engineering Education*. The focus is on the *fundamentals* — that is, on foundation ideas. For undergraduates, the foundations lie in the early-level teaching on which environmental engineering education is based. For engineers in practice, they represent basic ideas, techniques and outlooks that complement continuing engineering education courses with a more detailed focus. Our task is to adopt a broad and searching attitude, to examine the fundamentals and see what they should be, avoiding any temptation to become involved in details.

As for "environmental engineering", it should be taken in a broader, rather than a narrower, sense. As well as the more directly-involved environmental engineers who deal with a variety of technical matters ranging from waste treatment and pollution control to impact assessment, it could be said that all engineers need to be at least well-aware of environmental issues and needs. In other words, all engineers need to be environmentally literate. Taking this broad sense, the workshop could be more fully titled "The Fundamentals Underlying the Environmental Education of Engineers".

The reason for focusing on "the fundamentals" arose from a growing suspicion some of us have had that although the number of environmental engineering courses has been increasing around the world, something was missing. Not that in themselves were the courses being presented and developed bad. Far from it — the very fact of the increase has been a proper response to the growing urgency of need, of the developing realisation throughout the world that the environmental problems facing us are becoming increasingly grave. Why, then, were we concerned? It was a suspicion rather than a clear and easily-stated understanding. What seemed to be going on was that the courses we were developing were producing engineers who no longer seemed to match the more urgent needs of the world, industry and clients. The mismatch was not so much in the area of technical capability as in a lack of some increasingly needed skills. It was as if the engineers we were producing were in a sense the same sort of engineer, though with new environmentally-oriented technical capability, at a time when the world was really demanding a fundamentally different sort of engineer. If this were indeed so, then the problem could not be dealt with by simply adding new courses to old curricula, no matter how good the courses might be. What was needed was a new look at the whole.

Engineering education is a complex task. Curricula are intricate, and piecemeal changes of any depth are far from easy. What seemed to be needed was an exercise where we could take time to be together and look at the whole from the beginning. Clearly, we could not deal in detail with environmental engineering education as a whole — the task would be vast, and the many different needs would make it impossibly diversified. But neither would it be the point. What was really required was to review the very basics, the foundation subjects on which the rest is built. For, surely, it would be at this fundamental level that any deep innovation, responding to a change in the world's requirements for engineering skills, must begin. Thus, the workshop is *not* a search for detailed curriculum changes. They will have to be worked out later, and locally. It is *not* an exercise in looking at innovative teaching techniques, important though they may be. It is an attempt to examine, very deeply, the underlying basics of what we do.

It may well be that the issue is ultimately seen to encompass more than environmental engineering. The change in the nature of professional engineers may be more pervasive. If this is so, so much the better. What we are able to determine and the insights we attain in the workshop may have wider implications than for environmental engineering education alone. But for us, it is important to try to keep the focus clearly on the specific task we have set ourselves — to examine the fundamentals of environmental engineering education.

Modern Problems and Changing Needs

If it is true, as I believe, that the world and its societies now require a different sort of engineer, then there must be reasons for the change. Most stem from one source — that the most urgent problems are now of a different kind.

To begin with, they are more complex. This is particularly true of environmental engineering. Where once factories and furnaces could operate with no thought to the consequences of pollution and the limitations on resources of material, time and space or of the people and societies with which they interacted, there is now an accounting, a balancing. As the cost of pollution, both past and present, becomes more clearly defined and obvious, systems of production and reception are seen in their totality. Loops are closed, and the complexity born of feedback and of a myriad of competing interactions reveals new problems, whose nature becomes more urgent as they become more difficult.

The increase in complexity goes further than environmental engineering. It has come to pervade the whole of technology, and it reaches far beyond. We are considering problems, though, need-driven problems as we perceive them, and not the world itself. The world has always been complex, but we seldom see it as it really is. We choose what to see, both as individuals and, through convention and fashion, as social groups. We interact with the world, but only see that part of it revealed through our worldview, our *weltanschauung*.

Thus, we have not seen complexity because we have not needed to, and we have not dealt with it because we have not had the tools with which to do so. Now, though, we are forced to look as we begin to sense the limits of our world system, while at the same time, through computers, we begin to have the tools needed to understand and handle complexity. A few only as yet, though. Of others we need, we particularly lack conceptual tools, which are necessary for understanding the world and setting up problems for solution (the clear formulation of a complex problem is often more difficult than its solution).

Indeed, I believe our ability to compute, to model and deal with information by electronic means has now far outstripped our ability to understand what it is that we model. The gap, and the real need, is conceptual and philosophical. In this area, we hardly know where to begin. A few brave souls, though, are trying to find a path through the blank areas of our understanding.

To return to the matter of why engineering problems are increasingly complex, it is partly a matter of need, and partly one of a new paradigm, a new way of looking at the world.

It is also a matter of engineering problems no longer being neatly packaged into technical issues. Much of the complexity seems to occur where traditional "technics" — that is, technical matters — impinge on and interact with wider systems. Where technics meet the natural and social environments, we have the characteristic complexity faced by environmental engineers (among others). Where they interface with ownership and capital, again the problems are complex, though the complexity is of a different kind.

It is precisely because engineers are being required to extend the boundaries of what they do into wider problems and into societal needs beyond immediate technical matters that another change arises in the nature of engineering problems. As well as increasing in complexity, they are increasing in breadth, in scope. This has implications for both knowledge and for the way in which engineers must work. Knowledge must be more broadly based, and there is an increasing need to work closely with a range of others, both professionals and otherwise.

Finally, the new types of engineering problems are no longer crisply defined. The boundaries of the systems are not clear-cut, and the value systems required are no longer easily quantified. Even where they are, we may well be working with many incommensurable values that cannot readily be compared with one another. The well-defined and obvious boundaries of a concrete beam, a connecting rod or an electric circuit are still there. They are very much a central part of engineering. But the boundaries of the appropriate systems to be considered when dealing with the interaction between a new dam and the natural environment surrounding it are not as clear. How far from the dam might the effects spread? What is their dynamic nature over time? Will major effects arise from seemingly minor changes to water temperature, food supplies, travel paths and so on? Or, because a dam is a major hazard and a risk assessment is necessary, how much detail should the assessment include? What are the possible effects of human error?

How can the risk be communicated with the people living in a possible flood path? There is no clear bound to the possibilities of analysis, no clear guide as to what should be taken into account, no obvious definition of system elements, boundaries or measures.

Through complexity, breadth and a lack of clarity, many modern problems differ significantly from traditional technical problems. At the same time, they are more difficult. Yet it is problems of this type that society is increasingly, and rightly, demanding that engineers should solve.

The Four Phases of Technology

To clarify ideas, it might help to think of technology as developing in four phases. Each new phase includes those preceding it, but adds a new direction or dimension (Elms, 1993).

Humans have always used technology. Even the most primitive of our ancestors used tools, prepared food and medicines, and made artifacts such as pots, clothing or weapons, often with great skill and artistry. In this sense, technology has always been with us and has pervaded our lives. It still does, but with the essential and important difference that whereas once there was an immediate relation between we humans and our physical surroundings, we are now part of a complex technology-based web. The change has been very great. It is really, from our point of view as engineers, a change in the way we approach technology and decide how and for whom we carry out our tasks.

Though historically the changes have been continuous, nevertheless it is helpful to regard them as occurring in four phases.

The first phase can be called *Immediate Technology*. Once, if we wanted to eat, we had to hunt, plant crops or herd animals, depending on our culture. There was a simple connection between our fundamental needs and their attainment. The causal links were short and immediate. The tools required for phase 1 technology were simple and available to all, even though the technological products, such as cave painting or the manufacture of poisons for hunting, could be sophisticated.

The next step, phase 2, relates to urbanisation and so can be called *Urban Technology*, even though it was a technology that related to cities rather than one used exclusively by them. The growth of cities coincided with the need to centralise administrative power. The earliest probably resulted from the first use of extensive irrigation. This could not take place without the use of a massive communal effort to construct and maintain canals and other aspects of irrigation, which in turn required centralisation and a bureaucracy. Other reasons for the growth of cities were the need to control large political groupings, and trade. (It should be remembered that, historically, cities were not always large — it is believed, for instance, that at the earliest stage for which archaeological records are available, some of the Greek "cities" had a population of about 25 people.) In phase 2 technology, the immediacy of the link between technology and people's needs was broken. Specialists built and manufactured, and mechanisms of trade developed. Technology was essential to the very existence of the growing web of society. However, the nature of technology was still quite different from modern practice, relating more to a combination of trade and artistry rather than to anything remotely like the engineering of today. Not that technology lacked sophistication — it was far from primitive. Significant advances took place in Europe, for instance, right through the dark ages and mediaeval times. However, construction and manufacture were still based mainly on rules of thumb rather than on rational analysis.

The third step, phase 3, brings us to modern times. It coincides roughly with the development of the industrial revolution in Europe and the growing use of energy. For our purposes, the most important aspect of phase 3 was the growth of scientific rationalism and its adoption for engineering planning and design. This is the point at which professional engineering, as we now know it, began to emerge. New analytic tools were developed, and engineering was no longer governed by arbitrary rules. The findings of science could be combined with measurements of material properties to allow a faster and more reliable extension of existing technology into new artifacts and processes. New branches of engineering came into being, such as aeronautics, electronics and tribology, and the movement was regularised and given added impetus by the developments of mass production and of national and international standards. The use of new energy sources, particularly those using fossil fuels, increased the role and capabilities of technology. And as society became increasingly urbanised, not only were people's lives more dependent than ever on technology, but also the causal chains linking what they did with their fundamental needs became longer and more complex. We can give phase 3 the name *Rational Technology*.

Nevertheless, there is a sense in which phase 3 technology is still simple, insofar as in its connectedness and its focus on the predictable and measurable it is straightforward. Causal chains are short, for the most part. As far as the analytic capabilities of engineers is concerned, technique has mostly emphasised the sophisticated analysis of relatively simple systems. For example, structural engineering deals with the analysis of individual structural elements at an increasing level of sophistication, particularly with the advent of modern computer codes. Yet the behaviour of an entire structure in an earthquake still cannot be modelled satisfactorily and, even if it could, there remains the underlying methodological problem that about 80% of failures are due to human error in design, construction or maintenance.

As another example of the limitation of phase 3 technology, consider electricity production and transmission. Thermal or hydro power stations can be designed remarkably efficiently, and sophisticated techniques exist for controlling transmission problems such as harmonics. Yet it seems far more difficult to plan for adequate supply capacity, or to evaluate alternatives as to their long-term effect on society or the natural environment. Techniques for handling such matters are primitive compared with those available for dealing with direct technical problems.

The existence of more complex problems and the growing need to deal with them indicate that we are now entering a fourth phase. To be sure, technology is changing fast. Its extent continues to grow, and the speed of change is increasing. More important, though, and at the same time less obvious, is that at a deeper level the very nature of the technology-related problems society is trying to deal with are undergoing a fundamental change. As discussed in the previous section, the new problems are broader, more complex and less well-defined than those of phase 3. They are pervasive and occur in all areas of engineering, and they are particularly characteristic of environmental engineering in its broader sense. The new phase, phase 4, can be called *Systems Technology*.

The discussion so far should not be taken to mean that complexity itself is new to technology. Rather, the point being made is that until recently, engineers have seldom needed systems approaches and that where they have been used, the results (as I have seen them) have generally been neither rigorous nor well-founded.

Characteristic Weaknesses of Engineers

Perhaps because engineering education for the most part deals with phase 3 problems, or even perhaps because of the self-selection of many of us as people who particularly enjoy technical problems, engineers are not always very good at dealing with phase 4 problems. Let me set down a brief and personal list of our shortcomings. Though there are many exceptions, we tend not to be as good as some other groups at:

- *Conceptual analysis* — We are better with numbers, calculations and spatial perceptions than we are with abstract and loosely-defined ideas. If young engineers and lawyers are in action together, the difference in their ability to handle complex concepts is very marked. It is not that the engineers are unintelligent — far from it. But their training has not particularly fitted them for that type of analysis.

- *Communication* — Many engineering students are not particularly good at either written or oral communication, though for the most part they seem to attain reasonable skills in practice. The trouble may relate to conceptual analysis, both directly, as communication involves the systematic mustering of ideas, and indirectly, in that it has been found, for writing skills in English at least, that ability to write well correlates strongly with how many books are read.

- *Relating to other groups* — Engineers, sure in their technical competence, are often less than tolerant of other groups and individuals who have a different approach, background and characteristic language.

- *Understanding limitations and underlying assumptions*— Though the immediate technical limitations of a piece of analysis and the assumptions on which it is based are generally well-appreciated, I do not believe engineers are particularly good at understanding the deeper methodological and philosophical issues underlying their work. It may relate to conceptual analysis. For phase 3 problems, most of which cover technically well-trodden ground, the problem is not especially important. However, it becomes more significant for the broader problems of phase 4.

- *Leading complex projects* — Though many complex developmental projects are led by engineers, there are many more cases where management is taken over by other professions. In some areas, this seems to be an increasing trend. Engineers sometimes become leaders more because of their individual natures than by reason of their training.

Causes and Symptoms

The focus of the workshop is on needs and ways of responding to them, and particularly on outcomes. However, to give a context to the needs and, thus, to consider the reasons for the workshop and the background thinking that led to its inception, it makes sense to look for reasons for the problems outlined in the previous section. Some are historical, some are attitudinal and some are educational, but all are interrelated.

Many of the causes stem from an attitude of progress, development and exploitation, which arose particularly in the western world and accompanied its development of technology and its increasing use of and dependence on energy. The world was seen to be a limitless source of whatever was required. There was an emphasis on exploitation rather than sustainability, on competition at the expense of cooperation, on short planning horizons at a time of dynamic and seemingly perpetual change, and on seeing and working with simple unbounded systems, with no concerns about boundaries, of what lay beyond the fence, or of tomorrow. It was a period of increasing specialisation, first of the operators and workers of the industrial revolution, but later of engineers, doctors, lawyers and other professionals to the extent that we became rather like a hive of specialised insects, each with its place. And yet, anomalously, specialisation and change — or, rather, the ability to adapt to it — do not belong together. They are, ultimately, incompatible. Despite this, engineering education still seems to focus on specialisation as we see, in New Zealand at any rate, an increasing proliferation of specialist subjects. The only restraints on this headlong progress and narrow focus seem to have been limitations of information-processing capability, communication and time to respond to change through social and economic means.

Of course, there are good reasons for specialisation. Specialists can be remarkably effective, and efficiency increases. Nevertheless, intense specialisation is vulnerable to change, and where it concerns people, there are moral and ethical issues to be considered as well.

To return to the reference to the historical approach of working with simple unbounded (and, thus, improperly defined) systems, it is heartening to see some determined attempts emerging to change to a different paradigm. I believe the viewpoints and system visions of Don Roberts (1990) and John Peet (1992), among others, are particularly relevant.

One problem that has emerged is that we seem to have come to a position where there is an increasing lack of balance between technics and policy. Our technical activities are increasingly out of control. Not only is political control uncertain at best, but we simply do not have adequate mechanisms and instruments for control, or any clear and agreed decision framework, despite the aims and results of the UNCED conference and Agenda 21.

The problems are ingrained and pervasive. They are also difficult, and they are grave in their possible results. Neither are they readily amenable to solution.

At the very least, though, we can order our own house and educate engineers in such a way that our capability is improved and matched to the real needs that face us.

Requirements

So far, we have considered problems. To deal with them, many things must be in place. Some are what the world needs, some our society. Others are needs of engineers, either as individuals or as a profession.

Looking first at the world's needs — there are so many — we must restrict ourselves here to what follows from the earlier discussion. There are three needs that have appeared. The first is a need for control — control on use and control on pollution. As this is a sociopolitical matter rather than one that can be dealt with by engineers, it is a requirement for understanding rather than for direct action. The second need is for sustainability, of life and resources of every sort, and here we are, surely, centrally involved. The third is for rehabilitation of damage, insofar as it can be achieved.

What, then, are the things engineers need to be able to do? In an arbitrary order, the items that have emerged are:

- the need to deal with complexity;

- the need to be able to take a long-term view;

- the need for criteria against which to be able to assess proposals;

- the need for guiding principles of ethics, equity etc.;

- the need for an ability to relate and understand, beyond our immediate specialisations;

- the need to be aware of systems and their boundaries; and

- the need for an organising principle to integrate individual specialisations together.

The list is by no means complete. It does serve to illustrate, however, that if the modern engineer has to have such capabilities, in addition to the more traditional technical skills we normally take for granted, then some very fundamental changes need to be made in engineering education.

A Change in Character

What we have been talking about is the need for a change in the character of engineering, and of engineers. This should not be taken to mean that all engineers should be different. Roberts (1990), writing along similar lines, believes that about a quarter of engineers should be trained in the new and generalist way he outlines, with the rest applying themselves to more traditional tasks. This relates very well to the idea of the four phases of technology discussed earlier. Historically, when phase 3 technology came into being and professional engineers were needed, they still had to work with, and indeed needed, phase 2-trained people, that is, technicians and tradespeople. Similarly, phase 4 engineers need phase 3 professional engineers to deal with the more narrowly focused technical problems that, increasingly, are there to be solved.

Nevertheless, the profession as a whole must change in character. The change has been described elsewhere (Elms, 1989) as a search for wisdom, in contrast to knowledge. There is, of course, nothing wrong with acquiring knowledge. The phase 4 engineer must go further. To knowledge must be added many things — value and an understanding of quality, for one. The ideas of quality management are closely related to what the phase 4 engineer, and in this case, the environmentally-educated engineer, needs to do. But, in addition, the new engineer needs strong communication skills, an ability to deal with large, complex and ill-defined systems, and a clear and far-sighted world view, which, together with a well-developed ethical stance, more than anything else characterises phase 4 engineering wisdom.

Conclusion

The new environmentally-educated engineers are, thus, so different in both skills and outlook that tinkering with an established course is no longer enough. That is why we need to re-examine the foundations, the fundamental early-level courses for environmental engineering education that set the direction for the remainder of undergraduate education. We must deal, too, with existing engineers as well as undergraduates. Many will want to change their outlook and acquire skills of the sorts we have been describing. Thus, our "foundations" must embrace both undergraduate teaching and continuing engineering education.

References

Elms, D G (1989). "Wisdom Engineering: the Methodology of Versatility". *International Journal of Applied Engineering Education.* 5(6): 711-717.

Elms, D G (1993). "The Case of the Missing Foundation: Systems Thinking as a Fundamental Skill". *Proceedings: AEESEAP/FEISEAP/IACEE International Conference of Engineering Education.* National University of Singapore, November 1993. 33-44.

Peet, N J (1992). *Energy and the Ecological Economics of Sustainability.* Washington DC: Island Press.

Roberts, D V (1990). "Sustainable Development and the Role of the Engineering Profession". *Proceedings of the FIDIC Annual Conference.* Oslo, Norway, June 1990.

The Need for Environmental Engineering Education Fundamentals

David Thom
WFEO Committee on Engineering and
Environment
Auckland, New Zealand

Abstract

Since the 1960s, engineering has lagged behind an accelerating social concern with a deteriorating environment. Out of this concern came "Our Common Future", the UNCED and the concept of sustainability. The implications of this for engineering have led to a number of statements by senior engineering bodies. These sum to a new role for engineers. Because ethics, values, attitudes and a new technological paradigm are implicit in the new role, it represents a change in engineering culture. A feature of the past 30 years has been the rate of change in the social value context of engineering. Driving forces are such that the rate of change will continue to increase. In the recent past, engineering educators have been adapting courses by incorporating a variety of environmentally-oriented material. In general, however, adapted engineering courses do not equate to the requirements now stated by the engineering bodies. Nor are they likely to meet the challenge posed by the accelerating rate of change. Engineering education needs to be visibly and actually based in the new culture.

Introduction

The practice of engineering has arrived at a fork in the road. The signpost to one direction says "sustainable development", a broad concept that encompasses economic and social wellbeing, as well as sustainable management of resources. The other points to an increasing isolation of technology from reality. Historically, engineering has been a principal agent of development. It must now become a principal agent of sustainable development.

My task is to discuss the need for environmental education in engineering and to deduce focusing questions that can be considered in the group sessions. Is there a need for environmental education in engineering? Thirty years ago such a question could not have been formulated. In engineering, it was "given" that there was no such need. Five years ago, I worked on studies of a severely degraded estuary that was the outcome of the engineering naivety of that time.

A growing discovery about the relationship between engineering and the environment was accelerated by the United States National Environment Protection Act of 1969 and its requirement for environmental impact statements. The saga of CFCs and ozone depletion, the prospect of climate change, ratification of the Framework Convention on Climate Change and Biodiversity Convention, "Our Common Future", the Report of the World Commission on Environment and Development (1987), and Agenda 21 itself all command attention to the relationship between technology and the natural world.

"Cleaner production", or manufacture with efficient use of resources and minimal discharge of waste, is an understood and growing application, as is life-cycle analysis, the study of the resource use and impact of a product from origin to discard. We can be sure that this 30 year voyage of discovery is by no means over. It began with the technology and the "golden age" syndrome of the early 1960s. Through the 1970s and 1980s, confidence in technology and those who applied it eroded. The UNCED was "an expression of technological disquiet", to use the words of the UN Undersecretary General for Policy Coordination and Sustainable Development. The voyage may be still in its early stages. A notable feature of the last 30 years has been the rate at which environmental concern has developed, even accelerated, through unpleasant discoveries, which usually resulted from ignorance of natural systems, failure to investigate potential impacts, or an over-confident neglect of what is now known as the "precautionary principle".

Since our planetary environment is now deteriorating rapidly, there is a general case for environmental education for all humankind. This case was made by the UNCED (1992), and Agenda 21 devotes a chapter to "Promoting Education, Public Awareness and Training" to "... achieve environmental awareness in all sectors of society on a world wide scale as soon as possible". To use another quotation that is right on target, "Education is critical for achieving environmental and ethical awareness, values and attitudes, skills and behaviour consistent with sustainable development". Stated in the baldest terms, the resources of nature, on which all human existence is dependent, will inevitably continue to decline while a shift to the concept of sustainable living takes place. But human population is now increasing at the rate of about one billion every eleven years. A billion approximates the human population growth of the two million years prior to the industrial revolution. This morning, there were a quarter million more people than there were yesterday morning.

Even in New Zealand, where our resources are now managed under laws that obligate sustainable management, ecosystems are in decline and we have restoration work to do. Agenda 21 advocates education about sustainability for all. We cannot make the transition without it, to a substantial degree, because this is not an issue of knowledge alone. Ethical awareness, values, attitudes and behaviour all require change. These are attributes of culture.

The concept of sustainable development, first advocated in "Our Common Future", represents a shift of huge proportions. It is a paradigm shift. But as the alternative to making the shift is disaster, we have to make it. We have to make it now because resource decline and population increase are on a collision course. These two factors combined are driving an accelerating rate of change. If, for engineering, the last 30 years have been a voyage and discovery of relationships between technology, society and natural resources, the next 30 years are likely to be a revolution.

The role of technology in the paradigm shift represented by the concept of sustainability is crucial. Without a consequential paradigm shift in relation to the role of technology, the transition to sustainability cannot be made. "Our Common Future" talked of the "re-orientation of technology, the key link between humans and nature". To make the transition, technology must become compatible with, supportive of and subservient to natural systems, including ecosystems. It must become supportive of positive social and cultural directions, which, like natural systems, will be under stress in the period of accelerating change. For technologists, this is the new paradigm, compared with the old paradigm of an unfettered technology. This is an enormous shift in fundamental standpoint. It is shifting the foundations of engineering culture.

Statements by the Engineering Institutions

The senior engineering bodies have not merely acknowledged that this is so, they have set out in forthright terms the future role of engineering. In the last three years, a number of unequivocal statements have stated the characteristics of a new engineering practice. The World Federation of Engineering Organisations (1991) said that education in the issues related to sustainability should be given the highest priority, and strongly emphasised research and development of sustainable technologies.

Early in 1992, the World Engineering Partnership for Sustainable Development (WEPSD) was formed by WFEO, the International Association of Consulting Engineers (FIDIC) and others. Analysis of Agenda 21 by the WEPSD identified a spectrum of 241 actions "most related to engineering". Since the UNCED, WFEO has again recommended the inclusion of principles and practice of sustainable development in the curricula of engineering education and training. The WEPSD (1993) sees a need to redirect engineering education to instill, early on, a respect and an ethical awareness for sustainable development at all levels in the education process, with the ultimate goal of building the needed capacity for all present and future engineers, men and women. A first step in redirecting the education of engineering will require the adoption of sustainability ethics within the profession. Sustainability calls for fundamental changes in personal and professional conduct. In 1991, FIDIC published its policy statement on the environment and has just published "The Consultant and the Environment. A Guide for Actions" (1994).

The Engineering Council of the United Kingdom (1994), the Engineering Society of Finland and the Central Union of University Engineers and Architects (1993), the American Association of Engineering Societies (1993), the Association of Professional Engineers and Geoscientists (Alberta), the Japan Society of Civil Engineers, the Institution of Engineers Australia (1993), and the Institution of Professional Engineers of New Zealand (1993) have all published guideline statements. UNESCO and UNEP have strongly encouraged environmental education in engineering, and UNESCO-sponsored teaching materials on "Selected Topics in Environmental Management" are currently under trial in Europe, Southeast Asia and the Pacific.

This is a solid spectrum of authoritative engineering and international opinion. The engineering statements describe an approach to the practice of engineering that is greatly in advance of the technological solution to a stated problem or objective that distinguished the engineering philosophy of the 1960s. They describe a new culture, because in the combination of values, ethics and behaviour they deal in the fundamentals of culture. As the American Association of Engineering Societies (AAES) says, "Sustainable development requires new ways to do business and demands dramatic changes in the culture of engineering".

There is a great deal of common ground in the statements, even when emphasis most relates to basic responsibilities. The FIDIC Standing Committee's "Guide to Actions", for example, is focused on engineering practice. Permeating the statements is the sense that engineering has been presented with a challenge to which the needs in response are clear. The notions of leadership, pro-activity, leading by example, becoming involved in and contributing to the total social effort towards sustainable development are common to all. The practice of engineering is seen as that of a profession that is environmentally well-informed, conceptually in command of the concept of sustainability and equipped with the motivation and the methodological tools to apply the concept. It is clear to the institutions that all this has major implications in the ethics, education and practice of engineering, and that leadership is an important component.

In ethics, the statements issue a challenge for a new position and basic depth of background that is new to an engineering profession reared on the notion that ethics is about codes dealing with relationships with one's fellow practitioners.

IPENZ refers to the need to develop and promote a sustainability ethic that has regard to ecosystem interdependence and biodiversity, the finite capacity of the environment and the rights of future generations — a question that is on the agenda of the WFEO Standing Committee on Engineering and Environment. The FIDIC Guide recommends that before a project is accepted, the adequate address of potential negative impacts should be assessed, and if reasonable efforts to ensure address are unsuccessful, an engineer should abandon the project. The Engineering Council of the United Kingdom (EC/UK) has raised the question of an obligation to be professionally competent to handle environmental issues.

WEPSD has stated that university curricula should be redesigned, existing criteria re-evaluated and practising engineers re-educated. Engineering professors should be targeted, students empowered as agents of change, and non-engineers educated in technical aspects of sustainable development. As an example of a specific action, WEPSD suggests the creation of a "Sustainable Management Assistance Corps" that picks up the pro-active, outward-looking theme. In the same vein, the Engineering Society of Finland talks of acting as an example and of participating in nationwide discussion.

FIDIC is among the most specific regarding curricula change. Education should include the integration of technology within social, cultural and economic dimensions. A multidisciplinary approach that incorporates socio-cultural demographic aspects is required to solve environment and development issues. Curricula should move towards the principles of sustainable development and expand to include ecological sciences, risk assessment and risk management. Greater emphasis is needed on systems and decision analysis, including application of environmental impact analysis (EIA). FIDIC also advocates the general theme that engineers should be environmentally well-informed, generally and specifically, on environmental trends and issues, especially as to developments in the application of Agenda 21. "Bridges and partnerships should be developed," says the FIDIC Guide, "to create national and regional centres of excellence in interdisciplinary research and education in environmental and developmental sciences." The interdisciplinary theme is another that recurs repeatedly in the engineering statements. AAES says that engineers must work with others to adapt existing technologies and create and disseminate new technologies, and that achieving global sustainability will require a multidisciplinary approach.

The EC/UK "Guidelines on Environmental Issues" sees engineering education in an overall context, as suggested, perhaps, by Agenda 21:

> *"Environmental awareness should be a prime subject of education and training at all levels, commencing at primary school and going on to Continuing Professional Development. The education and training for the student, graduate and professional engineer at any level must be designed to provide an appropriate and mature understanding of environmental matters and the relevance of the work that engineers do and the likely impact on the environment."*

The EC/UK says that employers perceive the need for cross-curricula "greening" of further and higher education and for staff development to raise environmental understanding and knowledge. Updating should be achieved through greater communication with industry about needs and development, more flexible delivery (e.g. modules and distance learning), staff secondments (e.g. two-way exchange with industry) and databases of updating material.

The EC/UK is not alone in suggesting that engineering education has a substantial interest in environmental education in schools, referring to the potential of "neighbourhood engineers" (a UK initiative), and pointing out that while there is an overwhelming supply of teaching material on "environmental issues, teachers will only select and use those projects they see as fulfilling a gap or need".

The EC/UK considers that initial formation (that is, education) in engineering should introduce basic understanding of the natural environment, pollution problems and the way in which engineers can deal with them within their particular discipline.

Postgraduate work should concentrate on in-depth knowledge and skills that relate to environmental policies, environmental audits and impact assessment, life-cycle analysis, recycling and resource management, and pollution control. Curricula should include reference to ethics, sustainability, ecology, natural systems and the decision-making process of project development. Within the education and training of engineers, there needs to be an appreciation of cost and a realistic method of cost-benefit analysis so that a reasonable balance between the demands of the environment and society can be obtained. "This area clearly needs to consider the case for sustainable development so that we do not compromise the needs of tomorrow by what we do today."

In statements about engineering practice, general themes also emerge. One of these is the need to carefully scrutinise projects at the outset. The AAES introduces long-term responsibilities:

> *"In planning for sustainable development, engineers need to examine fully and systematically the aggregate long-term consequences of decisions, in terms of both time and space, and the alternatives which may lead to more environmentally sustainable choices."*

(The use of alternatives is another theme.)

"Engineers", says AAES, "need to acquire more environmentally sensitive and responsive tools to integrate environment and social conditions into market economics".

The FIDIC seeks a conceptual grasp of resource management:

> *"The consulting engineer should consider the use, processing, transportation and consumption of resources as a closed loop to the extent possi-*

ble, rather than a once through system. Throughout the process, waste should be minimised, and the by-products from manufacturing and consumer use must be recycled to the extent possible and feasible as recovered resources."

The approach is also advocated by other engineering bodies, which pick up the proactive/leadership theme in regard to cleaner production, sustainable technologies and "more with less resources, less energy consumption, and less waste generation", to quote the AAES.

The Working Environment of the Engineer

Country reports received at intervals from members of environment committees of WFEO and the Federation of Engineering Organisations of Southeast Asia and the Pacific (FEISEAP) show clearly that the legislation and policy that guides environment and resource use worldwide continues to expand, strengthen and broaden its control. This is the umbrella under which technology is applied. At this present time, it is growing rapidly because countries are in the process of ratifying the climate change and biodiversity conventions and shaping the policies that will reduce greenhouse gas emissions under the Climate Change Convention. The practising engineer must know the duties, requirements and intention of resource legislation as never before.

Ethics is back in fashion. It is taught in professional courses in medicine, law and business. The medical, legal and accountancy professions have faced costly ethical problems that have driven the reform of teaching and practice. Ethics is seldom taught in engineering courses, and the engineering profession has, so far, avoided major ethical debate because the responsibility for selection and application of technology is socially diffused. But two points should be noted. The first is that the trend illustrated by the history of environmental impact assessment (EIA) and by major technology-related problems is towards clarification of responsibility. The professional engineer will soon be required to demonstrate the requisite level of environmental skill as a basis for acceptance into an engineering institution. The second is that the concept of sustainable development introduces new moral issues related to choices and decisions about "the ability of future generations to meet their own needs". More than the relentless updating of codes of ethics, engineers need the capacity and the knowledge of technological/societal history and interaction to be able to debate and handle ethical issues at the personal and professional level. We can expect that engineers will become ethically bound to practice in a way that promotes the concept of sustainability.

A major feature of the engineer's working environment is the directions being taken by the employers of engineers — government, local government and industry. In the fast-developing scene of the past 30 years, it has often been the practising engineer, exposed at the front edge of development, who has had to adjust practice and learn new skills, such as EIA. Consulting engineers are among the first to change, which gives cause for careful attention to FIDIC's "Guide to Actions". But in the past, the external environment has sometimes been confusing because directions were not agreed. That is no longer the case. Major employers of engineers are moving in the same direction, even if the rate of movement varies, grappling with environment and sustainable development, developing policies, corporate statements and management plans. The environment has entered total quality management and standards specifications. It became the commitment of major business in 1991, when the International Chamber of Commerce launched "The Business Charter for Sustainable Development" (1992).

Research and development of technology is generally shifting towards sustainability, whether we consider the automobile industry, developments in use of sustainable energy resources, the drive towards increased energy efficiency, the uptake of cleaner production or the expanding databases that offer increasing accessibility to information in these fields. Major industries, like our farming industry in New Zealand with its debates on sustainable land use, are studying the whole question of what constitutes sustainability in their terms. This is evidence that society at large is starting to grapple with the concept, supported by media that saw long ago that the environment was a major news issue. Organic produce is in increasing demand in the world's food markets and environmentally-friendly products require more and more shelf space in supermarkets. Society is environmentally conscious, and will, inevitably, become much more so.

Accelerating Change

The introduction to this paper referred to a 30-year voyage of discovery about the relationship between technology and the natural world in which confidence in technology eroded and engineers were in a defensive/reactive situation. Responses fell behind the target, because the target continued to move forward.

Indicators suggest that in the next 30 years, the rate of change will be further increased by population growth multiplied by rising living standards (30 years to 2025; 8.5 billion people, up 70 percent; 18 cities over 10 million; 5.5 billion in cities). All the factors I have referred to in the working environment and the focus now being given to new, cleaner and sustainable technologies, to ever more efficient use of resources and to finding the means of applying the concept of sustainable development, mean that the technologist will become a key agent of change, concerned with the development and application of new, rather than old, technologies. This will require the capability to assess alternative technological options within an economic, social, cultural and environmental context.

Engineering Education and Perceived Need

While the present status of environmental education in engineering has been considered in some countries, and even some aspects of status in some regions, surveyed information is insufficient for authoritative statements that have studied support. The view of the present status has, necessarily, to be compiled from a few country studies, and informed opinion. UNESCO has maintained a very long interest, and almost 20 years ago published a working party report on the desiderata of environmental education in engineering. On the evidence of UNESCO's recent initiatives towards worldwide publication of teaching materials on environmental management for engineers in both text and distance learning modules, its view has remained unchanged. The UNEP Industry and Environment Office maintains a keen interest and is strongly supportive of this workshop.

In August 1991, Dr Upali Kurrupu, programme specialist in the UNESCO Regional Centre for Southeast Asia, made a limited survey of Schools of Engineering in Australia, Malaysia, New Zealand, the Philippines and Thailand. Dr Kurrupu advised that six subject areas for priority action had been identified:

- management of solid wastes;

- municipal water and waste water treatment;

- agricultural, ground water and soil pollution;

- selected topics in environmental management;

- air pollution control; and

- industrial pollution and related clean technologies.

Respondents were asked whether postgraduate courses in these subject areas were considered necessary and useful, whether their faculties would be interested in contributing to production of the materials and whether they would like to use the materials developed in their schools. All respondents stated that the environment was a major concern in their school, but opinion was divided on the question of sufficient courses. New Zealand and the Philippines did not consider there were. As to whether the need was greatest at undergraduate or postgraduate levels, the consensus was that there was a need at both levels. Significant points to note about the survey are that it was directed at educators and not to the professional institutions, and that replies were in the context of the areas advised for priority action. These had been selected from UNESCO information and would represent a considered judgement on priorities in the region.

Worldwide, educators have agonised over growing pressures to build environmental subjects into engineering courses. But if something was to be added, what could be left out? Dandy and Daniell (1992) reviewed the situation in Australia, noting that nine undergraduate courses in environmental engineering had been established since 1990. Seven of these were based in a department of civil engineering, with one in a school of chemical engineering and one in a school of environmental engineering. Although common course material could be recognised, and course structures were similar, there was less commonality than existed between courses in traditional fields like civil and mechanical engineering. Some had a greater emphasis on traditional engineering subjects. Others allowed considerable choice and the possibility of majors in ecology, biology or chemistry, as well as civil or chemical engineering.

After visiting seven Australian universities (not necessarily those surveyed by Dandy and Daniell), Professor Craig, Professor of Environmental Management at the Tamaki Campus of the University of Auckland, noted that environmental courses run from a specially-formed multidisciplinary department or division were far more successful than those run through coordination of established science or engineering departments (Craig, 1993).

Discussing "greening" the undergraduate curriculum, Professor J R Duffell (1990) noted that there was a need to include environment in all disciplines across the arts and science divide. There was much already of an implicit nature in engineering courses on environment — engineering science modules and applied subjects in civil, mechanical and building services engineering contain environmental matters, such as energy efficiency, water pollution control, highway and public health engineering. Professor Duffell quoted a planning and environmental technology paper in a second year honours course that embraced land use planning, social cost benefit analysis, environmental economies, law, and pollution of air, water and land.

Environmental adaptions of engineering courses appear to be recent, vary widely in content (with a variation that probably reflects local environmental priorities) and to be an outcome of the tension between increasing pressure on the traditional curriculum, and perceived market pressures to incorporate environmental subjects. Admirable as the initiatives are, the variation demonstrates, amongst other things, uncertainty as to the philosophical base of engineering, now effectively redefined by the engineering statements.

The Gap

One of the themes of this paper is the rate of development of the environmental situation. Both the environmentally-adapted engineering courses and the statements by the engineering institutions are mostly products of the past two to four years. There has not, as yet, been meaningful communication between engineering practice and engineering education. This workshop may be one of the first bridging discussions between considered opinion emerging from practice, as represented by the statements, and educationalists grappling with an extremely difficult situation.

The difference between the role and needs of engineering, as presented by the statements, and the present status of educational adaption, is large and obvious. It is a difference compounded by an accelerating rate of change. Will students of the most advanced adapted course meet the demands of say, ten years hence, in 2004? Can even continuous adaption match the rate of change? This is impracticable. It is also improbable, and for fundamental reasons.

The statements describe the practice of technology under the over-arching influence of natural systems, in a multidiscipline context, selected as much by social, cultural, ethical, environmental and economic factors as by the engineering objective.

The problem is this: the existing structure of education is based on the technological paradigm of the pre-sustainability period. There is not time for adaption, and the adaption of the past 30 years has not kept pace with the shift in social values. A new engineering culture cannot be produced in time from adaptions presented in an educational environment that is a fundamental expression of the pre-sustainability technological culture and paradigm.

I have quoted the perceptive comment by Professor Craig that courses run from a specially-formed multidisciplinary department or division were more successful than those run through coordination of established departments. Gardner (1993) discusses a "green" civil engineering degree from the University of Brighton in which the objective is to approach a single subject area and modify the course content. Graduates study the fundamentals of environment and ecology through a three-year programme. The approach contrasts with the more general development of engineering ability in an engineering context offered by other environmental engineering courses. The University of Brighton courses directly apply the principles that all construction should in future be the best practicable environmental option; that is, the best available technologies that do not involve excessive costs and which use the precautionary principle should be used.

This approach is, philosophically, on a much more secure base than the development of environmental ability in an engineering context, which does not (philosophically) accept the paradigm shift discussed earlier and is still projecting the "old" technology culture.

Conclusions

- Engineering institutions wish to fashion a pro-active, leading role for engineering. Engineering education, like engineering practice, has reached a watershed represented by the scope of a new engineering philosophy and culture — the application of sustainable engineering, characterised by:

  — preservation of natural systems as the primary objective;

  — selection and application of technology based in social, cultural, economic and environmental parameters;

  — values and attitudes based in the ethics of sustainability;

  — leadership and contributions to development of sustainability policy; and

  — facility in multidiscipline operations.

- The challenge of sustainable engineering involves all facets of engineering, and a strategic approach is needed. There is a need for education and practice to work closely together. Education has a critical role, but this role needs to be seen in the context of overall strategy and the contributions of professional practice. This brings into question:

  — the profession's interest in primary and secondary as well as tertiary education; and

  — the profession's position on ethics, qualification and continuing education.

- It is essential to consider carefully the implications of rate of change, since the question of what fundamental approaches to education are required to equip engineers for coping with rapid change may need consideration.

- The total resources of the engineering profession, including education, are limited in relation to the scale of the task. This is an argument for the strategic approach, since new skills and teaching may be needed within education as well as practice.

- Adaption of existing engineering curricula cannot meet the requirements of the new culture, partly due to rate of change, but mostly because of mismatch with new cultural requirements. In addition, the signals to students, the community and the profession must be clear. Undergraduates who are taught about sustainable development by a multidiscipline faculty and who mix with natural scientists and sociologists in the daily round of lectures and laboratories will absorb a view of the relationship between technology and the world that is different from that derived from the traditional engineering faculty.

- None of the above implies that the teaching of technology should be softened or reduced. Equipping graduates with training for an era of rapid change may mean prioritising teaching on principles rather than details. Utilisation of new "sustainable" technologies may mean abandoning teaching in "old" technologies and developing teaching and methodologies that enable discrimination and selection of "new" technologies. The UNESCO 1991 education priorities for the Southeast Asian region (management of solid wastes, municipal water and waste water treatment, agricultural, ground water, and soil pollution, selected topics in environmental management, air pollution control, industrial pollution, related clean technologies) may still be entirely valid. The question that may arise from strategic considerations is whether the responsibility for education that relates to applied practice should be carried by the profession.

- It may be difficult for education, as it is for practice, to shed the sense of a defensive position — the result of the past 30 years of the environment versus development debate, with engineering seen as an agent of development. Should the engineering profession be able to emerge visibly as the agent of "sustainable development", the debate will be over.

The Focusing Questions

- How can education best respond to the requirements expressed for new values, attitudes and paradigm for applied technology in the statements by the engineering bodies?

- What are the impediments to this response?

- Looking at engineering education overall from the pre-tertiary level to qualification and continuing professional development, what strategic elements, responsibilities and approaches are recommended?

References

American Association of Engineering Societies (1993). *Policy Statement on the Role of the Engineer in Sustainable Development.*

Association of Professional Engineers and Geoscientists of British Columbia (1992). *Report of the Taskforce on Sustainable Development.*

Craig, J L (1993). *Environmental Science, Technology and Engineering in Australia: A report on visits to seven Australian universities.* Auckland: University of Auckland.

Dandy, G C and T M Daniell (1992). "A Review of Undergraduate Engineering Degrees in Australia". *National Conference Publication 92/5.* Barton, ACT: Institution of Engineers, Australia.

Duffell, J R (1993). "Sustainability and Engineering Activity". *Environmental Education in Higher Education Curricula.* Engineering Seminar, University of Hertfordshire (Hatfield Campus), July 1993.

Engineering Council, UK (1994). *Guidelines on Environmental Issues.* Draft, Revision A, 28 January 1994.

Engineering Society in Finland and the Central Union of University Engineers and Architects (1993). *Joint Statement on Technology and the Environment.*

FIDIC Standing Committee on the Environment (1994). *The Consultant and the Environment: A Guide for Actions.*

Gardner, P (1993). "BEng (Hons), MEng Environmental Engineering". *Environmental Education in Higher Education Curricula.* Engineering Seminar, University of Hertfordshire (Hatfield Campus), July 1993.

Institution of Engineers, Australia (1993). *Environmental Principles for Engineers.* Barton, ACT: Institution of Engineers, Australia.

Institution of Professional Engineers of New Zealand (1993). *Environmental Principles for Engineers.* Wellington: Institution of Professional Engineers of New Zealand.

International Chamber of Commerce (1992). *From Ideas to Action.* Oslo: ICC Publishing and Ad Notam Gyldendal.

UNCED (1992). "Agenda 21 and Other Outcomes: The Non-binding Statement of Principles on Management, Conservation and Sustainable Development of All Types of Forests, Convention on Biological Diversity, Convention on Climate Change". *UNCED Outcomes.* Wellington: New Zealand Ministry of External Relations and Trade and Ministry for the Environment.

World Commission on Environment and Development (1987). *Our Common Future.* Oxford: Oxford University Press.

World Engineering Partnership for Sustainable Development (1993). *An Action Plan for Sustainable Engineering.* Agenda Material for Planning Retreat, April 1-3, 1993. New York: United Nations.

World Federation of Engineering Organisations (1991). *The Arusha Declaration.*

Sustainable Development, Engineering Education and Activity

Roger Duffell
Department of Civil Engineering
University of Hertfordshire
Hertfordshire, England

Abstract

This paper is concerned principally with a view of engineering, engineering education and sustainable activity in the United Kingdom. A synoptic review of current environmental issues and the response of the engineering profession in its widest sense is presented. It highlights the tentative impetus for greening undergraduate curricula and the response by industry to environmental issues. The importance of engineers adopting a high profile in public affairs to convey concern and commitment to sustainable development is stressed. The author calls for opportunities in engineering education for the synthesis of rational and intuitive thinking in solving complex problems. The author will attempt to bring the audience up to date on the pending publication, on 1st September 1994, of the Engineering Council's Guidelines to accompany the Code of Professional Practice on Environment introduced in October 1993. The national seminar on Environmental Education in Higher Education Curricula for the Engineering Sector "UK plc", held under the aegis of the Centre for Environmental Education in July 1993, is also described.

Introduction

Environment remains to the fore on the political agenda, even given the present world recession and grave anxieties about unemployment. Concern on global warming has greatly increased since the Montreal Protocol was signed in 1987 and the now-virtual phasing-out of CFCs in the so-called developed world. The repercussions of the Exxon Valdez oil spill in April 1989 and the fires in the Gulf oil fields in 1991 have done much to focus attention on the environment. The pace of political change over the last five years has graphically heightened the effects of pollution in Eastern Europe. The words "sustainable development" are now better understood: "... that which meets the needs of the present without compromising the ability of future generations to meet their own needs" (UNCED, 1987), and should guide individuals and societies to ethical human activity. The greening of industry continues as firms seek "market share" and undertake environmental audits against a background of an articulate and discerning public. The passing of the 1990 Environmental Protection Act in the UK and efforts to value the environment in economic terms are also matters of concern for engineers in their initial formation and continuing education.

Thom (1992), refers to the "Earth Summit" in June 1992, which concluded with a declaration enshrining 27 principles to "emphasise the fundamental need to integrate environmental factors into all development decisions if catastrophe is to be avoided".

He picked out 11 of these of direct or indirect concern to all engineers, from which the author highlights three by way of illustration:

4 — achievement of sustainable development to go hand in hand with environmental protection;

6 — special needs of least developed countries and the most environmentally vulnerable to be given priority; and

17 — undertaking environmental impact assessments.

Arising from the declaration was Agenda 21, a pathway to sustainable development in the 21st century — an action programme for now to the end of the millennium. Chapter 36 of Agenda 21 addresses re-orienting education, increasing public awareness and promoting training.

After Rio (1992), the World Engineering Partnership for Sustainable Development (WEPSD) was established as a non-profit making organisation under the chairmanship of the President of the World Federation of Engineering Organisations (WFEO). It has established four committees: executive, resource development, sustainable development and, finally, a partnership advisory committee — to develop relationships with other organisations involved with sustainable development. The founding partners in WEPSD are WFEO, FIDIC (International Federation of Consulting Engineers), UATI (International Union of Technical Associations) and CIESIN (Consortium for International Earth Science Information Network).

Institutional Responses in the Engineering Scene

The United Kingdom Engineering Council (hereafter EC/UK) advised those devising enhanced or extended degrees, thus:

> *"It is becoming more widely accepted that the solution to engineering problems cannot be separated from other economic and environmental consequences and account must be taken of the non technical disciplines which contribute to the success of an enterprise."*

This post-dates similar sentiments by the Institution of Civil Engineers and the then-Joint Board of Moderators (ICE, IStructE) who, in 1985, reaffirmed that matters of environmental concern be considered for inclusion in accredited degrees. The FEANI Code of Conduct for Engineers (1988) includes within its terms:

> *"... strive for a high level of technical achievement which will also contribute to and promote a healthy and agreeable environment ... be conscious of nature, environment, safety and health and work to the benefit of mankind."*

The EC/UK booklet "Engineers and the Environment" (1990) asked individual engineers to study and take account of issues such as global warming, energy efficiency and waste production, and challenged engineers in looking to the 21st century to update themselves on environmental and other issues. At the design stage, engineers are asked to consider ten fundamental questions with environmental overtones (see Table 1). The EC/UK, jointly with the then-Fellowship of Engineering (now the Royal Academy of

Ten Steps to Environmental Excellence	Ten Questions for the Green Designer	Towards The 21st Century — Recommendations to Engineers
source: *"The Green Capitalists"*, Elkington and Burke (1989)	source: *"The Green Designer Exhibition"* Design Council, London (1987)	source: *"Engineers and the Environment"* Engineering Council (1990)
Develop and publish an environmental policy	Is there a risk of disastrous failure?	Update themselves on environmental issues
Prepare an action programme	Could the product be cleaner?	Work to develop a "green" code of practice
Ensure responsibility for environmental agenda is vested in top (board) management	Is it energy efficient?	Apply the code as a professional discipline
Allocate adequate resources	Could it be quieter?	Set environmental improvement objectives
Invest in science and technology	Should it be more intelligent?	Design for (and with) the environment
Educate and train at all levels	Is it overdesigned?	Specify energy efficient equipment
Monitor, audit and report	How long will it last ?	
Monitor evolution of the green agenda	What happens when its useful life ends?	Contribute to the environmental debate
Contribute to environmental programmes	Could it find an environmental market?	Promote sustainable development in order to safeguard the future
Help build bridges between the various interests	Will it appeal to the green consumer?	

Table 1: *Objectives and contents for environmental courses.*

Engineering), sponsored a high-profile conference "Growth and Prosperity in a Green and Pleasant Land", whose prime objective was to demonstrate that economic growth and environmental protection can complement each other (Fellowship of Engineering/ EC 1991). One of the authors, Peter Chester of National Power under "Industrial and Engineering Perspectives", suggested engineers should help "fashion a technologically sensible future not simply respond to current pressures and expedients", and asked engineers to get on top of the science, to think and act globally and to seek the best practical environmental options rather than the best ones technically.

Following a consultation period the EC/UK launched its Code of Professional Practice (Table 2) on Environment (1992), on 6th October 1993. A task force was charged with developing draft guidelines on environmental issues, which will no doubt address the implementation of environmental aspects at undergraduate and postgraduate levels through selected case studies with probable thrusts based on life-cycle costing, legislation, environmental economics and environmental impact assessments. The *Guidelines* were launched on 1st September 1994 at the Institution of Civil Engineers in London.

1	Role	Engineers should seek ways to change or improve designs, methods, processes, operations, products, discharges and wastes to enhance or to reduce damage to the environment.
2	Approach	Engineers should use their professional judgement and experience to maintain a balanced, disciplined and comprehensive approach to environmental issues.
3	Assessment	Engineers should carry out systematic and imaginative environmental reviews of their work.
4	Cost Benefit	Engineers should seek the optimum combination of cost, social benefits and environmental protection.
5	Management	Engineers ensure that the management function embraces appropriate environmental policies and practices.
6	Ethics	Engineers should be familiar with The Engineering Council's Code and Rules of Conduct set out in the Council's byelaws.
7	Law	Engineers should be aware of the legal framework within which they are working.
8	Professional Development	Engineers should keep up-to-date by seeking appropriate education and training on environmental issues and associated techniques.
9	Communication and Public Awareness	Engineers should seek to provide balanced information to society on environmental issues.

Table 2: *Engineering Council's nine-point Code of Professional Practice: Engineers and the Environment* (EC/UK, 1992).

In its ongoing deliberations, the Institution of Civil Engineers' Education, Training and Membership Committee took the view that it wished to survey the extent to which environment had permeated the honours degree curricula. The Joint Board of Moderators took this up and issued a questionnaire in April 1994, with the assistance of the author, to all heads of department offering courses accredited by the JBM in civil, structural and building services engineering. An 80% response from departments was forthcoming and the questionnaire was extended into the realms of postgraduate/post-experience courses and seminars/symposia.

The analysis has not yet been undertaken, but it is clear that departments, in varying degrees, have warmed to the explicit focusing of environmental issues and concerns from hitherto implicit positions. Interestingly, to the question "what proportion of staff have a keen interest in explicit inclusion of environmental material in the undergraduate curriculum?", the proportion averaged 60% in the range 30% to 100%. Those taking a neutral view averaged 30% and those "hostile" averaged only 5%. The charge, therefore, that civil, structural and building services engineers are anti-environment has been largely laid to rest — the author has no doubt, though, that asked five years ago this question would have elicited significantly different responses. The suggested reason for the shift on the part of academia is not unrelated to the popularity of environment in the curricula of schools and colleges and, therefore, its recruitment potential. It also offers the opportunity to engage in cross-disciplinary engineering formation. Very much related to this is the change in name of many departments/schools, especially in civil engineering. The current JBM annual report contains the following departmental titles as at 31st December 1993:

- Civil Engineering   24
- Civil and Structural Engineering   4
- Civil and Environmental Engineering   2
- Civil Engineering and Building   3
- Engineering   8
- Other   16

The "other" embraces Architecture, Surveying, Environmental Technology, Building Science/Technology etc., in various combinations.

Valuing the Environment

Those involved in transport infrastructure planning have long grappled with the elusive problem of putting a value on the environment. Pearce et al. (1989) have attempted to develop an environmental economics framework drawing on a number of case studies involving water pollution and traffic noise effects on property values. They conceived a "payoff matrix" based on optimistic and pessimistic policies towards problems in the environment and anticipatory or reactive actions to confront them. They proceeded to show that anticipatory actions would entail less financial cost in the long run against six criteria:

- time preference (discounting);
- cost escalation;
- uncertainty;
- information by delay;
- irreversibility; and
- sustainable development.

The value of the environment can be seen in either the costs of anticipatory measures or the costs associated in cleaning up the pollution. Broad-brush calculations suggested environmental protection measures costing between 1% to 3% of GDP.

The acronyms BATNEEC (best available technology not entailing excessive cost) and BPEO (best practicable environmental option) are assuming a common currency, involving not only economic and engineering judgement but also environmental sensitivity. Clift (1991), chairman of the-then SERC (Science and Engineering Council) Clean Technology Unit's management group, has said:

> *"A clean technology is a technology which provides a service or product in a way which reduces costs (as opposed to 'Clean Up technology' which*

> *may reduce environmental damage but increase costs). The ICI 'LCA'
> Ammonia Process is a well known example of a Cleaner Technology;
> Flue Gas Desulphurisation is an obvious example of a Clean Up Tech-
> nology. Profligate Environmentalism is the opposite of Cleaner Technol-
> ogy; it describes any practice which increases costs and also increases
> environmental damage or resource consumption ... usually arises where
> a pressure group addresses a single perceived environmental problem
> but fails to think through the implications of its proposed 'solution'."*

Sir John Fairclough, Chairman of the EC/UK (1991), in his paper "Technology Opportunities", closed with these words:

> *"Environmentalists talk of pollution as an external diseconomy. For too
> long all of us have seen environmental matters as of concern only to
> others. There is a simple definition of marketing which states that no
> decision should be taken without an assessment of the likely impact of
> the decision on the customer. For customer read environment. We have
> to internalise the environment so that everyone becomes aware of the
> impact of their own actions and of the contribution they can make. Inter-
> nal charging systems for pollution loads are a way of bringing the mes-
> sage home ... My concern is that developing a system for valuing the
> environment, which is sufficiently robust and simple to apply, will take
> some time."*

Greening the Engineering Curriculum

The JBM questionnaire survey referred to above largely follows from developments
within academia, and this section is about "greening" of undergraduate curricula where
there is a need to include a study of environmental issues in all disciplines across the
arts and science divide. In 1991, the PCFC (Polytechnics and Colleges Funding Council) asked all institutions to embrace environmental quality in their strategic plans, and
in that year HM Government set up an environment committee to develop policies for
"greening the curriculum". A working document with that title was produced by Dr Ali
Khan (1991), at the University of Hertfordshire, under the auspices of the then Committee of Directors in Polytechnics (CDP). Translating its sentiments into the engineering curriculum is, to say the least, challenging, principally because of the pressures
already on the curriculum and, arguably, attitudes of the accrediting bodies and engineers themselves.

The author's university hosted one in a series of ten seminars devoted to the inclusion
of environmental education in higher education curricula for engineering courses. The
seminar attracted 65 delegates (10 industrialists, 8 from governmental and NGO bodies
and 47 academics from 32 universities) and comprised five sessions — contextual,
industrial pointers, academic developments (2) and integration methods. Under academia,
eleven courses were highlighted, either of recent foundation or those proposed for the
1993/94 session. Of these, four were new courses, based in chemical, manufacturing
systems and civil engineering departments, but having common elements with existing
traditional single-discipline courses in the earlier parts of the course. Of the remainder,
developments included core and electives in subjects such as environmental impact

assessment, law and the environment and life-cost analyses. Integration methods were explored in interdisciplinary design projects with strong environmental themes, basic science of the environment through CAL packages for all engineering undergraduates in one university and the unifying themes of public inquiry role play and noise studies. Another six course developments are incorporated in the seminar report, which is now with the publishers.

Industrial pointers at the seminar were provided by Norsk Hydro, Lucas Industries, Rank Xerox, Nuclear Electric and Three Valleys Water. All but the first co-sponsored the event. Speakers focused on their organisation's engineering activities. They indicated that significant attributes desired of undergraduates in their initial formation were environmental law and economics, environmental assessment, cradle-to-grave philosophy and integrated pollution control.

Notwithstanding the outcome of the above "research" exercise, there is much already of an implicit nature in engineering courses on environment — engineering science modules and applied subjects in civil, mechanical and building services engineering, contain environmental matters, such as energy efficiency, water pollution control, highway and public health engineering and so forth. Within the author's own discipline and up to the 1991/92 session, all students studied planning and environmental technology (Table 3) in their second-year honours course, embracing land-use planning, social cost-benefit analyses, environmental economies, law and pollution of air, water and land. It is a paired option, with foreign language study, because of pressures on the curriculum, but now it may also be taken as an elective in the final year. At second year level, environment is addressed in the product design specifications for the year 2 interdisciplinary design project activity, across all degrees in the School of Engineering. Finally, engineers should be instructed in physics, chemistry and biology to underpin, in an informed way, scientific understanding of environmental issues. The author is currently addressing environmental issues through named route opportunities within his honours degrees in civil and also in building services engineering.

Another significant development that effectively parallels AEESEAP's Christchurch workshop is the establishment in 1993 of the Forum for Environmental Engineering Education, which is holding its first conference in September 1994 in Scotland at the University of Abertay, Dundee. This body has come about through the common interests and concerns of the younger academics, and its first conference is supported by Ove Arup and Partners Scotland, the McGraw-Hill Book Company, the City of Dundee District Council and the University's Wastewater Technology Centre. The programme draws on examples of environmental engineering curricula and educational approaches across the main engineering disciplines and moves to international comparisons with papers from India, Papua New Guinea and Hungary. Its concluding session surveys industrial and professional requirements. The author is aware that of all the accrediting bodies under the aegis of the Engineering Council, the JBM has received a substantial number of new course proposals and modifications to existing accredited courses, which threatens to overwhelm it. It is rightly concerned about academic quality issues and the resourcing implications of such proposals.

EC/UK's Ccde of Professional Practice on Environment was the precursor to the guidelines being produced on such approaches and includes case studies drawn from engi-

Aims and Content of undergraduate course module "Planning and Environmental Technology"	Aims and Content of Continuing Education Schools for Civil Engineers "Engineering the Environment"
aims/outcomes: to enable student to appreciate the social context in which civil engineering and construction is undertaken to acquaint the student with the overall need to protect and enhance the environment through appropriate construction activity to lay down the principles of sustainable development and thus to ensure that at all stages external costs are considered as far as contemporary developments will allow	**aims/outcomes**: to instil a corporate approach to environmental design and problem identification through selected case study material to raise the level of awareness and knowledge of practical environmental issues in their political, social and economic setting to emphasise the need to communicate and justify one's proposals/actions
Content History of Town and Country Planning Structure Planning Traffic Noise and Visual Intrusion Air Pollution Urban Ecology and Ecosystems Social Cost Benefit Analyses Water Pollution The Greening Business Environmental Law Environmental Impact Assessment Energy conservation Land reclamation Construction Economics/GDP Infrastructure planning Airport Location	**Content** Ecology/ecosystems Ethics in civil engineering Human Resources in civil engineering Biological indicators of water quality Land Reclamation and ecology Nature Conservation and River Engineering Biological indicators of air quality Waste Disposal and Management Habitat creation Landscaping of roads Landscaping of Industrial Developments Three dimensional design in urban building Social planning and community architecture Justification and accountability in construction activity Public inquiries Noise and Visual Intrusion from traffic Environmental Impact Assessment

Table 3: *Environmental pointers for engineers.*

neering practice. This will be appropriate in terms of continuing education up to and beyond the CEng and IEng qualifying stages. The author can visualise the coming together of engineers in weekend workshops/master classes on environmental topics along the lines of his fifteen successful residential schools for civil engineers to date (1992). Held under the joint auspices of the ICE (and former IMunE) and the Field Studies Council, over 200 graduate and chartered engineers have engaged in lectures, workshops and field work (over three or four days) on the topics shown in Table 3. They have been supported by around 50 organisations — local authorities, public bodies and consulting practices. The schools could easily be adapted to cater for the needs of other engineering disciplines.

The Institution of Chemical Engineers (1992) is, arguably, leading the professional nominated engineering institutions within EC/UK circles in giving environmental guidance to academic establishments seeking honours degree accreditation. It rightly resists the temptation to prescription or mandating institutions to include environmental matters in a rigid format. Instead, it offers guidance using a matrix (Table 4) under three headings: awareness, understanding and in-depth knowledge, through either incorporation in existing studies or enhancement through specific topics (optional or mandatory). This process is set to accelerate following publication of the Toyne report (1993), setting out an agenda for Environmental Responsibility in Further and Higher Education.

The WFEO statement (1991) recommended governments to adopt sustainability as the guiding ethic and said it should be given the highest priority in education. Apropos undergraduate academic formation it stated:

> *"There is a need to provide sufficient content in engineering education to ensure that graduates have a mature understanding of environmental values and an ability to identify, manage and incorporate these aspects into development projects. Curricula should include courses in ethics,*

	Incorporated in existing studies (using or indicating environmental examples)	Enhancement through specific topics (introducing optional or mandatory topics)
Awareness (to demonstrate that the subject exists, is important and its relevance to chemical engineering)	Basic chemical engineering Legislative procedures Engineers in society (interaction with other issues, environmental impact)	Historical review Legislation Impact of products (cradle to grave analysis) Nuisance Renewable/non-renewable resources Risk acceptability
Understanding (the principles underlying the topic, and knowledge of its application within chemical engineering)	Basic chemical engineering Bio sciences Particle technology Computing (environmental modelling) Economics Design studies (integrated pollution control)	Geographical (global, local physical and social) Prevention and control techniques (Assessment techniques, eg environmental audits) Treatment techniques (eg gas, liquids, solids) and case studies (eg nuclear, pharmaceutical, combustion) (Cleaner technology)
In-depth knowledge (more detailed knowledge of the topic leading to the ability to apply it to real situations)	Basic chemical engineering (via design project and other projects)	

Table 4: *Environmental protection education working party matrix (IChemE, 1992).*

*sustainability, ecology, systems of nature and the impact of individual
choices on nature and people."*

Quite an undertaking and challenge!

The Greening of Industry, Public Relations and High Profile Activity in Engineering

By being seen to have an environmental concern, industry, in selling its products and
processes, increases market share, aided by growth in financial investments with an
environmental emphasis. Elkington and Burke (1987) chart the growth of green capi-
talism and conclude by suggesting ten steps to environmental excellence (Table 1).
Most of these embrace a more ethical stance on the part of employees and employers.
Most major companies now have an environmental policy statement and public bodies,
such as Nuclear Electric plc, go to considerable lengths (under statute) to consult with
bodies such as the Countryside Commission and English Nature (formerly the Nature
Conservancy Council) on proposals or actions likely to affect the environment. Interestingly, the Commission recently gave its qualified approval to a proposal to develop
the largest UK wind energy generation farm in Keilder Forest, which has been approved under the County Structure Plan by the Northumberland County Council.

A significant development in the field of environmental economics is the growth in
environmental reports accompanying annual reports and accounts. A publication by the
Chartered Association of Certified Accountants (CACA) gives force to this emerging
phenomenon (1990). Professors Owen and Gray report that British Telecom won, for
the second year running, the Environmental Reporting Award organised by the above
professional body (1994). These authors report on the trend to more transparency and
site reporting. They compliment ICI thus:

> *"... Indeed, ICI makes the only attempt to achieve some integration of
> financial and environmental data on addressing environmental issues
> specifically in the annual accounts ..."*

Of most significance is their comment:

> *"Generally, the reports fail to provide an impression of how moves to-
> wards truly sustainable business practice will affect operations. One fur-
> ther weakness is the lack of attention paid to the financial consequences
> of the firm's environmental initiatives and a failure to link the environ-
> ment report to the main accounts."*

They commend for certain aspects National Power, Anglian and Severn-Trent Water
Authorities and British Gas, all major national companies, for their environmental
reports.

The environment now permeates most engineering thinking, and the Construction Industry Environmental Forum was set up in 1991, principally by the Construction Industry Research and Information Association (CIRIA) supported by the Building Services Research and Information Association (BSRIA) and the Building Research Establishment (BRE). It operates under six technical areas:

- energy use;

- global warming and climate change;

- resources, waste and recycling;

- pollution and hazardous substances;

- internal environment; and

- planning/land use and conservation, legislative and policy issues.

It has established itself as a leading body and has an impressive programme of seminars and workshops on ecolabelling, life-cycle analysis, waste management, etc. A publication from CIRIA (1994) is worthy of particular mention for its currency in adopting a cradle-to-grave philosophy for civil engineering and building products.

Further sources of information are the various awards containing successful case studies incorporating environmental protection, enhancement and conservation through engineering activity. The EC/UK's own Environment Award Scheme was instituted in 1991 with sponsorship from British Gas "to encourage good practice in the application of engineering for the protection of the environment". Attracting around 70 entries, the 1993 award winners were:

- first, a waste concrete recovery plant;

- second, conversion of liner board to 100% recyclable material; and

- third, a water quality data logger system.

The Royal Society of Arts (London) runs its Better Environment Awards for Industry annually, which embraces four categories: pollution abatement technology, green products, environmental management and appropriate technology.

The Institution of Civil Engineers (ICE) Infrastructure Planning Group produced its third report, the subject being pollution and its containment, which drew on 40 case studies of environmental conservation provided by its local associations. The annual British Construction Industry Awards were instituted in 1988 and are sponsored by 100 organisations, including *The Daily Telegraph*, *New Civil Engineer* and *New Builder,* and attract well over 100 entries for the coveted Civil Engineering, Building and Small Projects awards. Besides the winners, many submissions receive commendations, having satisfied in whole or in part the design criteria: "fitness for purpose, performance, appearance and environmental harmony, economy of labour and materials, benefit to the community".

Two recent developments in the ICE are of significance. The first is the promotion of an international conference on Wetland Management in 1994 with emphasis on geomorphic, hydraulic and hydrologic behaviour and the consequent implications for practical management solutions. The second development is that for its meeting in September 1994, council has a substantial agenda item on environment. It is in two parts — an information file on major environment issues and key aspects, followed by selected issues for debate. The first item, for which council approval is needed, lays the ground for an environmental file to be serialised in the new quarterly proceedings *Civil Engineering*. It will probably contain the following sections:

- Introduction;

- Policy Issues and Sustainable Development;

- the European Economic Community;

- Engineering Issues (emanating from the work of the group boards on energy, ground, maritime, transport, structural and building and, finally, water);

- Recycling Construction Waste, Solid and Liquid Household Waste;

- BS7750 (Environmental Management Systems Standard); and

- Bibliography.

Prepared by the Institution's Secretariat in external affairs, it will stand testimony to the work of the civil engineer in and for society and will be a timely and complementary document alongside the Engineering Council's Guidelines (for its Code of Practice — Environment), which will be launched on September 1, 1994, as it happens at the "Civils" HQ in London. The Civils is also promoting a series of half-day seminars, the inaugural one being on "Contaminated Land Treatment" with the official launch by a Minister of HM Government in November 1994.

The introduction of British Standard BS7750 (1992), the first in the world on environmental management systems, will afford companies the framework for the assessment, control and monitoring of their impact on the environment and for developing and enhancing standards. It is a natural and timely "extension" of the earlier BS5750 Quality Assurance Standard introduced in 1988, one to which many organisations now aspire. Two of the ICE's Environmental Panel members are on working groups of the British Standards Institution pilot programme for the draft BS7750. In a 1993 initiative, the Institute for Environmental Assessment undertook an environmental audit (EA) of UK industry (Thompson, 1992), which produced a response from 210 firms out of around 1000 contacted. While some industrial sectors had made more progress than others, overall 50% had environmental policies in place, 23% had policies scheduled for future implementation and only 21% had none. One wonders about the situation among the 78% who did not respond. The EAs undertaken were in descending order: legislation compliance (93%), policy compliance, waste/energy, liability and, lastly, product/cradle-to-grave (34%).

An Educated and Ethical Way Ahead

Population growth, people's material expectations and their realisation through technology and engineering provide an overwhelming challenge to engineers to devise ways of promoting sustainable development. Much of the foregoing discussion has been about ways and means of achieving this, but the most important aspect is in the formation of attitudes — here education has a vital role to play. In this synoptic review of developments in the UK, the author has been greatly influenced by Capra (1983), who suggested:

> "*What we need, therefore, is not a synthesis but a dynamic interplay between mystical intuition and scientific analysis ... To achieve such a state of dynamic balance, a radically different social and economic struc-*

ture will be needed; a cultural revolution in the true sense of the word.
The survival of our whole civilisation ... will depend ultimately on our
ability to adopt some of the yin (female) attitudes of Eastern mysticism;
to experience the wholeness of nature and the art of living with it in
harmony."

Much the same thinking pervaded Frye's paper (1991) on a 21st century perception of ethics. He suggested that:

"learning is, or at least should be, something that happens throughout
life ... It raises those issues some five to ten years ahead with the express
purpose of stimulating, creating and facilitating change."

Frye foresaw two levels of meaning and perception — lower (direct experience) and higher (intuition). Somehow, engineers and their educators/facilitators have to be involved in these developments if they are to play their part in this new age of enlightenment. Hopefully, this paper will contribute to that process and demonstrate that ethical thinking and action is at work in the engineering profession in the UK, be it in academia or industry. The environmental challenge is daunting, if not overwhelming, as portrayed in "Beyond the Limits" (Meadows et al., 1992), the sequel to the 1972 Limits to Growth study (Meadows et al., 1972). The gap between the developing and overdeveloped world has widened in those intervening years and the time remaining to take radical action is reducing at an increasing rate. Capra, Frye and Meadows have put the issues simply and starkly.

Finally, in this overview, whither the engineering institutions in the contemporary scene? By their very nature, they are august bodies with an understandable tendency to caution until scientific/engineering evidence of causes and effects have been established. That said, there is the all-pervading duty to serve society and all living beings. Osborne and Sankey (1991) undertook a study in Scotland that included an exercise into the response of the national professional bodies to environmental content of qualifications and policies. The results for the engineering and built environment sectors (see Figure 1) indicate a varied, if overly cautious, response on the part of most institutions/institutes, with IChemE, InstEDs, RTPI and RIAScot to the fore. Appropriately, further "green shoots" have subsequently appeared. The speed of change is accelerating as engineers and engineering organisations realise the importance of sustainable development and environmental protection. Christchurch 1994 is a significant watershed in which the author is privileged to be a part through the good offices of AEESEAP and WFEO. He hopes his contribution will help encircle this "only one Earth".

Sector	Professional body	Environmental content of qualification						Environmental policies						
		0	1	2	3	4	5	0	1	2	3	4	5	6
Engineers (17)	Biological Engineering Society	■						■						
	The Engineering Council		■	■		■			■					
	Heating, Ventilating and Domestic Engineers - National Joint Industrial Council	■						■						
	Institution of Agricultural Engineers	■										■		
	Institution of Chemical Engineers (IChemE)				■	■	■	■			■	■	■	
	Institution of Civil Engineers		■					■						
	Institution of Electrical Engineers	■						■					■	■
	Institution of Electronics and Electrical Incorporated Engineers	■						■				■	■	
	Institution of Engineering Designers (InstED)	■						■				■	■	■
	Institute of Hospital Engineering	■						■						■
	Institution of Mechanical Engineers				■								■	
	Instiiution of Mechanical Incorporated Engineers	■												■
	Institution of Mining Electrical and Mining Mechanical Engineers		■						■		■			
	Institution of Mining Engineers	■							■					
	Institution of Nuclear Engineers	■						■						
	Institution of Structural Engineers				■							■	■	■
The built and designed environment (10)	Architects & Surveyors Institute		■	■		■								■
	The Chartered Institute of Building			■	■				■				■	■
	The Chartered Society of Designers	■						■			■			
	Incorporated Association of Architects & Surveyors		■		■				■		■			
	Institute of Building Control		■					■						
	Institute of Housing			■				■						
	The Landscape Institute			■					■			■	■	■
	Royal Incorporation of Architects in Scotland (RIA Scot)		■		■	■	■		■	■		■	■	■
	Royal Town Planning Institute (RTPI)		■		■	■			■		■	■	■	■
	The Royal Institution of Chartered Surveyors		■			■		■					■	

KEY

Professional qualification including environmental content

0   No such qualification offered

1   Awarded by professional body examinations only

2   Awarded by taught course plus professional body examination

3   Awarded by exemptions based on professional experience

4   Awarded by exemptions based on qualifications

5   Awarded by another route

Environmental Policies

0   Does not have environmental policy (or did not respond to question)

1   Has environmental policy

2   Has been subject to an environmental audit

3   Has Green Charter

4   Has Code of Practice for members

5   Has guidance service for members

6   Has provided other information

Figure 1: *Responses of professional bodies to environmental issues.*

References

British Standards Institution (1992). *Environmental Management System Standards.* London: BSI.

CACA (1990). *The Greening of Accountancy.* London.

Capra, F (1983). *The Tao of Physics.* London: Flamingo/Fontana Books.

CIRIA (1994). *Environmental Handbook for Design and Specification of Civil Engineering and Building Projects.* Vols I and II. London.

Clift, R (1991). "Profligate environmentalism". *The Chemical Engineer.* February: 3.

Committee of Directors of Polytechnics (1991). *Greening the Curriculum.* May 1991. Working Document. London: CDP.

Department for Education (1993). *Environmental Responsibility — an agenda for further and higher education.* London: HMSO.

Duffell, J R (1987). "A balanced environment — civil engineering in its social and political context". *Municipal Engineer.* 4(February): 50.

Elkington, J and T Burke (1987). *The Green Capitalists.* London: Victor Gollancz. 228-237.

Engineering Council/UK (1983). *The Enhanced and Extended Undergraduate Engineering Degree Course.* London: Engineering Council.

Engineering Council/UK (1990). *Engineers and the Environment — some key issues.* London: Engineering Council.

Engineering Council/UK (1992). *Engineers and the Environment Embryo Code of Good Practice.* Discussion document. London: Engineering Council.

FEANI (1988). *Code of Conduct.* Tract 04.04.88. Ref DB/cc No. 242. Paris.

Fellowship of Engineering/EC (1991). *Growth and Prosperity in a Green and Pleasant Land.* London: Engineering Council.

Frye, M (1991). "A 20th century perception of ethics for the individual, the community and the RSA". *Royal Society of Arts Journal.* December 1991: 17, 21.

Gray, R (1994). "BT turns its rivals green". *Sunday Times.* 7 April, 1994.

Institution of Chemical Engineers (1992). *Teaching Environmental Protection within Accredited Degree Courses.* London: Institution of Chemical Engineers.

Meadows, D H (and others) (1972). *The Limits to Growth: A Report for the Club of Rome's Project on the Predicament of Mankind.* New York: Universe Books.

Meadows, D H, D L Meadows and J Randers (1992). *Beyond the Limits.* London: Earthscan Publications.

Osborne, M and K Sankey (1991). *Towards Environmental Competence in Scotland.* Scottish Enterprise.

Pearce, D, A Markandya and E B Barbier (1989). *Blueprint for a Green Economy.*

London: Earthscan Publications. 11, 19.

Thom, D (1992). "Engineering and the Rio Declaration". *WFEO Newsletter*. No. 4.

Thompson, D (1992). *Environment Auditing in UK Industry*. Horncastle, Lincolnshire: Institute of Environmental Assessment.

World Federation of Engineering Organisations (1991). *Statement on Environment and Development*. London: WFEO, ICE.

Environmental Engineering Education: Turn to Face the Sun

Gary Codner
Department of Civil Engineering
Monash University
Melbourne, Australia

Abstract

Sustainability as the way of the future was the clear message to come from the United Nations Conference on Environment and Development (1992). Our vision should be that by the year 2010, all engineers should adopt and implement the concepts of sustainability as a normal part of their professional activities.

To achieve this vision, a paradigm shift is required on the part of engineers. This change must occur at all levels within the profession, that is, in professional organisations, practising engineers, educators and students. Attitudinal change must be the focus of current activities, for without it the move towards sustainability will not occur. The issue of an environmentally competent engineering work force is addressed.

Professional organisations need to provide a leadership role for the profession in achieving the above vision and moving towards sustainability. IPENZ, IEAust and EC/UK have all started down this road — others need to follow their lead.

Education for sustainability is seen as a key issue and is addressed at undergraduate, graduate and continuing education levels. It is recommended that higher education institutions become signatories to the Talloires Declaration, which is a declaration by university presidents for a sustainable future. It is seen as essential that professional engineering organisations provide some guidelines for the inclusion of environmental education into engineering courses.

We have the vision. What we need, and must have, is the resolve and effort to make it happen.

The Need for Paradigm Shifts

"Turn to Face the Sun" comes from the conclusion of a paper by Thom (1994) called "The New Technical Culture", in which he states that:

> *"Engineers can either turn to face the sun* [an apt metaphor, since the sun is the basis of sustainability], *or continue on the road charted as 'disquiet' by the UN Undersecretary-General. A conscious choice is required, and it is needed now. Choice of the right path requires thinking about the nature and philosophy of engineering that has not been done before. Far from being beleaguered and unappreciated, engineers hold in their own hands the prospect of a new culture whose potential far exceeds the contributions of the past."*

As a corollary to this, if you feel the sun on your back, then you are going in the opposite direction and away from sustainability. For this reason, the title of the paper is felt to be appropriate — the choice is ours and we need to turn and feel the sun on our faces.

Officially known as the United Nations Conference on Environment and Development (UNCED), the Earth Summit emphasised the fundamental need to integrate environmental factors into all development decisions if catastrophe is to be avoided. Presently, there is general acceptance by the engineering profession of the concepts of sustainability. Indeed, the Institution of Engineers, Australia (IEAust) "Environmental Principles for Engineers" (1992) has been well received by the profession, other professional organisations and environmental NGOs. However, there is almost a total lack of translation of concepts into actions to achieve sustainability. This lack of action is attributed to two basic reasons — first, a lack of understanding of and commitment to sustainability, and second, that the way to translate sustainability ideas into specific actions is not understood and is difficult, particularly at the level of the individual engineer. The first problem must be overcome before the second aim can be achieved.

It is the thesis of this paper that if engineers wish to be relevant in the future, they must wholeheartedly embrace sustainability and implement it through engineering practice. The community will insist that decisions and projects move towards sustainability. A paradigm shift must occur in the way in which engineering is practised and will require an awareness of the importance of the topic on the part of individuals. It will be necessary to develop sector-based sustainability codes, guidelines and, hence, solutions.

Education will be essential in the move towards sustainability. This must involve improved environmental education within single-discipline undergraduate engineering degrees, continued development of the evolving undergraduate environmental engineering degrees and continuing education activities for practising engineers.

Sustainability is the way of the future. Our vision should be that, by the year 2010, all engineers should adopt and implement the concepts of sustainability as a normal part of their professional activities.

To achieve this vision, a paradigm shift is required on the part of engineers. This change from an old to a new technical culture is the subject of a paper by Thom (1994). The basis for the paradigm shift must be an "attitudinal and behavioural change" by engineers, without whom the vision will not be achieved. This change must occur at all levels within the profession, that is, in professional organisations, practising engineers, educators and students. Clients must also appreciate the need for sustainability. Attitudinal change must be the focus of current activities, for without it sustainability will not occur.

The year 2010 appears an excessively long way into the future. However, the magnitude of the task should not be underestimated as it requires policies, strategies and actions by a large number of organisations and individuals in many countries. For example, two years after the Earth Summit, little has occurred within the engineering profession to move towards sustainability.

Background to Sustainability

Sustainability is defined here as the ability to *maintain a high quality of life for all people, both now and in the future, while ensuring the maintenance of the ecological processes on which life depends and the continued availability of the natural resources needed.* Sustainability is *the ability to maintain a desired condition over time.* Sustainable development *is a tool for achieving sustainability,* not the desired goal.

As pointed out by Disinger (1990), sustainability is not a new concept. However, the language and directions have changed over recent times. The "modern era" of sustainability basically began in 1980 when the World Conservation Strategy was published. That document initiated worldwide discussion about the requirements for achieving sustainability, particularly about the need for development to be sustainable. *Our Common Future*, the final report of the World Commission on Environment and Development (1987), better known as the Brundtland Report, raised the profile of sustainable development.

Resulting from the Earth Summit, the Rio Declaration (or Earth Charter) sets out 27 principles that should govern future development. Actions needed to accomplish this are contained in a number of documents, notably Agenda 21, which can be seen as an operational plan for moving humankind into the age of sustainability. Although not legally binding, Agenda 21 has tremendous importance since it reflects the consensus agreement of 178 national delegations about the need for achieving sustainability and the key issues that must be addressed to reach that goal.

The Preamble to Agenda 21 conveys the following message:

> *"Humanity has reached a turning point. We can continue with present policies which are deepening economic divisions within and between countries — which increase poverty, hunger, ill health and illiteracy, and cause the continuing deterioration of the ecosystems on which life on earth depends, or we can change course. We can inextricably link development with protection of the environment and give greater attention to these linked issues. In this way, we can perform the essential tasks of fulfilling basic needs, improving living standards for all, and better protecting and managing ecosystems."*

In short, we must turn to face the sun.

Achievement of sustainability will require a global partnership between governments, non-governmental organisations, and the wider community. The World Engineering Partnership for Sustainable Development (WEPSD), initially developed to present unified engineering thinking on Agenda 21 (Carroll 1993), has since focused on five main issues that need to be addressed in moving to sustainability. These are to:

- develop sustainable planning processes;

- develop and apply technologies suitable for the capacity of a country;

- advance industrial ecology and sustainable productive systems;

- develop and make use of information that will enable the user to consider the long-term environmental consequences of each alternative; and

- redirect engineering ethics and education for sustainability.

Carroll (1993) states that the WEPSD is looking at the possibility of developing regional centres to help carry out these programmes. To achieve this, it is working with WFEO, the Third World Academy of Sciences and the World Bank (through the bank's Global Environmental Facility programme).

An Environmentally Competent Engineering Work Force

The World Federation of Engineering Organisations (WFEO) submission to the Earth Summit in 1992 stated that:

> *"Engineers have the potential and the duty to be a major influence in the achievement of the primary goals of the future: a sustainable habitat for all life, and one that continues to allow mankind to achieve his potential and to enjoy the process of living."*

As a result of this submission, Agenda 21 explicitly addressed the important role of engineers in achieving sustainability. It identified two broad programme areas:

- improving communication and cooperation among the scientific and technological community, decision makers and the public; and

- promoting codes of practice and guidelines related to science and technology.

To achieve this, engineers need a mature understanding of environmental and social values and the ability to identify, manage and incorporate these aspects into engineering practice. Compliance with legislative environmental requirements is only one facet of environmentally responsible engineering (Institution of Engineers, 1992).

Following the lead of the New Zealand Institution of Professional Engineers (IPENZ), the 1993 Annual General Meeting of the Institution of Engineers, Australia approved the following resolution:

> *"That Council acknowledge the leadership role the engineering profession must play in attainment of sustainable development and that Council develop special plans to achieve this leadership role and report regularly to the members."*

As a result of the resolution, a Task Force on Sustainable Development was set up for a two-year period (1994/95). The Task Force will develop guidelines for the consideration of sustainability and ask all national committees and societies to use them to determine how sustainability can be applied to their technical area. While it is essential that the concept and need for sustainability is understood, the real need is for actions at the workplace that help the individual engineer practice engineering to achieve sustainability.

IPENZ has realised the importance of the sustainability issue and has proposed restructuring the organisation to reflect that concern. In addition, the IPENZ Standing Committee on Engineering and the Environment has recommended that the mission statement become (IPENZ, 1993):

> *"To advance the profession of engineering by providing leadership in the sustainable use of the Earth's resources."*

In October 1993, the United Kingdom Engineering Council (EC/UK) launched its Code of Professional Practice for Engineers and the Environment, which aims to encourage greater awareness, understanding and effective management of environmental issues (Engineering Council, 1993). By following the actions in the code, the EC/UK suggests that registrants will "be able to progress the broader debate over how we may achieve sustainable activity, and in so doing make a contribution to the stewardship of the earth." The EC/UK nine-point Code of Professional Practice on Environmental Issues states that engineers should:

- work to enhance the quality of the environment;

- maintain a balanced, disciplined and comprehensive approach;

- make systematic reviews on environmental issues;

- balance economic, environmental, and social benefits;

- encourage management to follow positive environmental policies;

- act in accordance with the codes of conduct;

- know about and comply with the law;

- keep up to date by seeking education and training; and

- encourage understanding of environmental issues.

These points are basically the same as those covered in a more prescriptive way by the Institution of Engineers, Australia in their Environmental Principles for Engineers, released in June 1992.

The IEAust Policy on Sustainable Development (IEAust, 1989) is currently being revised to a Policy on Sustainability, based on Agenda 21 and the Rio Declaration, by the Institution's National Committee on Environmental Engineering. The draft policy recommends actions for individual members to adopt in the practice of engineering that leads to the achievement of sustainability. It states that individual members will be encouraged to:

- develop and promote a sustainability ethic;

- act with integrity, objectively and ethically, remembering their responsibility to the community and to future generations;

- apply the precautionary principle in their activities;

- urge clients or employers to incorporate sustainability objectives into design criteria, and to prevent or minimise the adverse environmental effects of engineering activities;

- include consideration of environmental effects and use of resources at all phases of planning and implementation of engineering activities;

- take reasonable steps to ensure that consideration is given to the consequences of all proposals and actions, direct or indirect, immediate or long term, upon cultural heritage, social stability, health of people and equity;

- identify and act to minimise potential environmental effects of engineering activities;

- recognise options and alternatives to improve sustainability, arising from examination of the basic functions and purposes of projects, or elements of projects, being considered;

- suggest alternatives to clients if the proposed engineering activity is likely to create unavoidable environmental risks;

- include consideration of costs and benefits relating to environmental quality and degradation in economic evaluations of engineering activities;

- recognise the right of the community to participate in project formulation and development and appropriately encourage such participation;

- recognise that compromising environmental standards in engineering activities is an inappropriate means of reducing cost;

- report on issues relevant to sustainability with honesty and integrity; and

- advise clients or employers of concerns about potentially unsuitable practices in engineering projects and recommend ways in which they could be mitigated.

Individual members, in their participation in the activities of the Institution and other bodies, and as individuals in the community, will also:

- improve the availability and quality of information available on sustainable practices and on requirements for achieving sustainability;

- provide information to clients, employers, the public and government about ways of improving the sustainability of engineering activities;

- assist in the development of improved indicators of sustainability; and

- promote and assist in the transfer of environmentally sound technology, cooperation and capacity-building.

The actions of these organisations form a sound basis for moving towards sustainability and set the framework for achieving an environmentally competent engineering work force. It is suggested that other professional engineering organisations should follow their lead.

All engineers should examine their daily work practices against the above list as a means of judging their practice of sustainability. In addition, individual engineers, companies and sector-based organisations should consider developing sustainable engineering work practice guidelines and codes. This approach has a bureaucratic sound to it; however, without these codes and guidelines, sustainability is unlikely to progress very far. This is the recent experience where the environmental principles for engineers have been well received by the profession but not translated into actions. The problem is that the principles are general and the problems of individuals and organisations are specific, thus requiring specific guidance. However, for example, it is not sufficient to instigate a series of seminars or workshops on efficient treatment of waste and refer to this as achieving sustainability as the emphasis is too narrow, even though efficient treatment of waste is important. There needs to be a paradigm shift away from "end-of-pipe" treatment to front-end waste prevention and minimisation of the use of resources and energy. The international increase in interest in clean production is a good example of a move to sustainability. The business community has realised that clean production can actually save money and is not always the economic burden that environment protection measures are often portrayed to be (Faulkner, 1992).

In discussing the subject of an environmentally competent work force, Cortese (1993) notes that the effects of pollution and waste on people and the environment and the depletion of natural resources are not included in conventional pricing of goods and services. He concludes that engineering students must be taught economic principles that properly account for these effects in both the short- and long-term and how current methods of short-term economic analysis mitigate against environmental protection. He further concluded that students should also be taught organisational strategies for management of the environment and the responsibility of the productive sector in minimising environmental impacts throughout the production cycle.

Coates (1993) notes that it may be difficult for some engineers to give automatic consideration to environmental factors because the training of engineers has traditionally pointed them in exactly the opposite direction, that is, away from the sun. The normal approach of separating the different factors and analysing each individually is unsuitable for consideration of the environment. A systems approach is preferred in which the overall objective of the project and the design conceived must be considered in total when assessing the environmental factors. Coates (1993) indicates that:

> *"... it must become normal for engineers to put before the client the best option for sustainable development within the terms of reference. If an even better environmental solution is available outside the terms of reference then the report must bring this to the attention of the client, with the cost implications and all other factors so that a rounded and fully informed decision can be taken before going ahead."*

Engineers must, therefore, have open minds, be prepared to use innovative thinking and be aware of society's needs. Coates (1993) supports the vision that sustainable development and environmental considerations need to become taken-for-granted as part of every engineer's everyday work.

The above concepts and actions should help develop an environmentally competent engineering work force. They will require and, hopefully result in, attitudinal and behavioural changes in engineers. The concepts outlined may be used as a base for judging engineering education at various levels.

Education for Sustainability

Institutional Framework

The major role of education and the raising of public awareness and training in relation to achieving sustainable development is noted in Chapter 36 of Agenda 21. Specific educational suggestions relating to sectoral issues are contained in other chapters. Some of the key actions from Agenda 21 are set out below. It should be noted that these actions were basically intended for governments. However, they can readily be interpreted as relevant to professional engineering organisations and educational institutions.

- National professional organisations are encouraged to develop and review their codes of ethics and conduct to strengthen environmental connections and commitment. The training and personal development components of programmes sponsored by professional bodies should ensure incorporation of skills and information on the implementation of sustainable development at all points of policy-making and decision-making.

- Countries and educational institutions should integrate environmental and developmental issues into existing curricula and promote the exchange of their methodologies and evaluation.

- Governments, industry, trade unions and consumers should promote an understanding of the interrelationship between good environment and good business practices.

- Aid agencies should strengthen the training component in all development projects, emphasising a multidisciplinary approach, promoting awareness and providing the necessary skills for transition to a sustainable society. The environmental guidelines of UNDP for operational activities of the United Nations system may contribute to this end.

Education at all levels of engineering is considered the key to moving to sustainability. The education requirements change according to the level of the individual person. For example, top management needs short awareness-raising seminars on the need for and principles of sustainability and why and how it will save money, particularly in a business situation. Those at middle management and technical levels need specific courses that target the technical problems in their particular sector. Formal graduate level degrees in environmental engineering will be needed to address the detailed technical solutions relating to particular environmental issues. However, such courses will need to be taught within the context of achieving sustainability and not simply the provision of efficient "end-of-pipe" waste treatment technology, important as it may be.

How can tertiary education institutions be encouraged to develop and provide the education required to move towards sustainability? A good start would be to encourage university and college presidents and vice-chancellors to sign the Talloires Declaration for an environmentally sustainable future. The Declaration is shown on pages 62-63. The Declaration was developed in October 1990 by 22 presidents, rectors and vice-chancellors of universities from all over the world and represents a list of actions that they would take to make environment and development education and research a central goal of their institutions. As at the end of 1993, 178 university presidents from 38 countries have signed the Talloires Declaration (Cortese, 1993). The Conference of European Rectors (representing 490 university rectors) has also endorsed the Declaration's principles (Cortese, 1993). The University of New South Wales recently (July, 1994) signed the Declaration and is believed to be the first university within Australia to do so.

The Declaration sets the corporate environmental image of the university and relates to environmental behaviour of the university and the academic content of courses.

The Talloires Declaration

The Declaration sets the framework from within which specific actions can be developed. It may, therefore, allow individuals to more readily progress environmental initiatives at the faculty or department level. The Declaration provides for the creation of programmes to develop the capability of academic staff to teach environmental matters. This "train the trainers" approach is considered essential for success in the environmental engineering education area. Engineering educators must understand what sustainability is, not feel threatened by it, and, particularly, not see it as a soft option that downgrades engineering technology or takes precious time away from hard engineering subjects within engineering degrees. This will require a shift in educational thinking. The problem is not easy to solve, since most academics relate very much to research in a specialist area and, therefore, do not have the time, or perhaps the interest, to keep in touch with international directions and thinking on sustainability. Tufts University in Boston has developed the Tufts Environmental Literacy Institute (TELI), which helps academics understand the need for including environmental learning in their curricula and then helps the academics develop the appropriate environmental content of the subject.

Environmental education for engineers at the undergraduate level is increasingly important as a way of instilling a sustainability ethic into future generations of engineers so that environmental considerations are second nature in the same way that economic and technical aspects are considered. This education needs to occur in both environmental engineering degrees, such as those newly emerging within Australia, and, perhaps more importantly in the single-discipline degrees, where it is almost nonexistent at present.

Luthy et al. (1992) suggest that we need to help students understand more of the possible leadership roles that they may assume and the need to become more involved in emerging social and political issues relating to their field. Students need to understand that environmental engineers should structure and articulate rational environmental policy and may work at the interface between policy and technology. This will help achieve the "attitudinal and behavioural" change mentioned earlier.

State of Environmental Engineering Education

Cortese (1992) notes that:

> *"... the current education of most environmental professionals is incomplete. Most are trained to deal with a subset of environmental problems, such as air pollution, water pollution, or hazardous waste, but not with environmental issues in an integrated, comprehensive fashion."*

Most technical courses stress "end-of-pipe" treatment (Soloviev, 1992), albeit that it is done to reduce pollution or to more efficiently treat waste.

Until recently, few curricula covered waste minimisation or the prevention of pollution through a redesign of the manufacturing process; in other words, cleaner production. A survey by USEPA's National Advisory Council on Environmental Policy and Technology indicated that major pollution prevention courses were taught in only 10 to 15 of the country's almost 400 engineering schools (Allen, 1992).

The Talloires Declaration

We, the presidents, rectors, and vice chancellors of universities from all regions of the world are deeply concerned about the unprecedented scale and speed of environmental pollution and degradation, and the depletion of natural resources. Local ,regional and global air and water pollution; accumulation and distribution of toxic wastes; destruction and depletion of forests, soil and water; depletion of the ozone layer and emission of "greenhouse" gases threaten the survival of humans and thousands of other living species, the integrity of the earth and its biodiversity, the security of nations, and the heritage of future generations. These environmental changes are caused by inequitable and unsustainable production and consumption patterns that aggravate poverty in many regions of the world.

We believe that urgent actions are needed to address these fundamental problems and reverse the trends. Stabilization of human population, adoption of environmentally sound industrial and agricultural technologies, reforestation, and ecological restoration are crucial elements in creating an equitable and sustainable future for all humankind in harmony with nature. Universities have a major role in the education, research, policy formation, and information exchange necessary to make these goals possible.

University heads must provide the leadership and support to mobilize internal and external resources so that their institutions respond to this urgent challenge. We, therefore, agree to take the following actions:

1. *Use every opportunity to raise public, government, industry, foundation, and university awareness by publicly addressing the urgent need to move toward an environmentally sustainable future.*

2. *Encourage all universities to engage in education, research, policy formation and information exchange on population, environment, and development to move toward a sustainable future.*

3. *Establish programs to produce expertise in environmental management, sustainable economic development, population, and related fields to ensure that all university graduates are environmentally literate and responsible citizens.*

4. *Create programs to develop the capability of university faculty to teach environmental literacy to all undergraduate, graduate and professional school students.*

5. *Set an example of environmental responsibility by establishing programs of resource conservation, recycling, and waste reduction at the universities.*

6. *Encourage the involvement of government (at all levels), foundations and industry in supporting university research, education, policy formation and information exchange in environmentally sustainable development. Expand work with non-governmental organizations to assist in finding solutions to environmental problems.*

> 7. *Convene school deans and environmental practitioners to develop research, policy, information exchange programs and curricula for an environmentally sustainable future.*
>
> 8. *Establish partnerships with primary and secondary schools to help develop the capability of their faculty to teach about population, environment and sustainable development issues.*
>
> 9. *Work the UN Conference on Environment and Development, the UN Environment Program, and other national and international organisations to promote a worldwide university effort toward a sustainable future.*
>
> 10. *Establish a steering committee and a secretariat to continue this momentum and inform and support each other's efforts in carrying out this declaration.*

Cortese (1992) noted that one possible reason for this situation is the traditional single-discipline nature of most university departments. This does not allow environmental expertise to be easily used across departmental or faculty barriers unless individual academics have a particular interest in doing so. As Page (1992) notes, it is necessary to have an "environmental champion" in the university to help catalyse action. In addition, multidisciplinary curricula are often considered soft and academically less rigorous than traditional single-discipline curricula. This aspect is noted by Cortese (1992) in relation to environmental courses.

However, it is essential to stop this way of thinking, as environmental problems are by their nature multidisciplinary and it is, therefore, necessary to develop multidisciplinary environmental education curricula and multidisciplinary research projects to underpin the solutions. The development of strategies for the prevention and/or solution of environmental problems will involve physical, natural and social science disciplines, and these need to be reflected in the curriculum. The task is to design and develop curricula that contain an appropriate and acceptable mixture of multidisciplinary and single-discipline skills in order that the graduate can not only discuss the broader issues, but actually contribute to the design and management aspects in their chosen field. It is essential to develop sufficient skills to produce the hard results in industry and the public service.

In relation to environmental engineering education, Page (1992) provides five basic questions to be addressed. These relate to the interdisciplinary nature of environmental education, how best to achieve it and how it can be most effectively focused towards achieving cost-effective, ecologically sustainable, technical solutions.

A number of reasons exist for the slow progress on environmental education. These include:

- a lack of a sense of urgency because awareness of the importance of the subject is not widespread;

- economic recessions make inclusion of environmental education requiring more resources difficult to achieve;

- lack of cooperation between industry and academia; and

- faculty resistance to change for reasons such as innate conservatism, lack of time, unavailability of suitable teaching materials, curriculum crowding etc.

Environmental Engineering Degrees

Graduates from environmental engineering degrees should have the ability to address environmental problems and to focus on practical solutions in a way that is currently difficult because of the single-discipline nature of most existing engineering curricula. There is a need to develop an engineer with a sound background in the physical sciences who also has a broad understanding of environmental, social and political processes and issues. The students must be exposed to a range of perspectives on environmental management and be able to communicate effectively with specialists from other disciplines, management, employees, individual citizens and community organisations. In other words, they need to embrace sustainability as a primary goal, thereby turning to face the sun. A graduate in environmental engineering should have the background to:

- understand the processes of natural and urban environmental degradation, its causes and possible solutions;

- understand the working environment, the health aspects and the relationship to the external environment;

- understand global environmental changes;

- assess the environmental impacts and effects of the processes of modern technology, industry, land development and aquatic development;

- incorporate environmental criteria in all stages of design, development and implementation;

- develop effective environmental and resource management systems;

- understand the development of environmental policy and its implementation; and

- understand the political, social and economic factors in environmental management.

However, it will not be possible for an environmental engineering graduate to cover all these topics in depth. A suitable environmental engineering curriculum should have a sound basis of mathematics and sciences, including ecology and biology. The curricula should contain a basic core of engineering synthesis and design, taught in a broader context than is currently achieved in single-discipline curricula, enabling the engineer to consider very different solutions to existing problems. In addition, a sound base in economics is required, together with environmental law, communication, ethics, social science and management skills. Luthy et al (1993) note that risk analysis and risk assessment also need to be included. They note that it is no longer sufficient to simply study fluid mechanics and chemistry as if all environmental problems were water-based. The total package must have an overriding philosophy for achieving sustainable development, as indicated throughout Agenda 21.

Codner et al (1993) outline some of the environmental engineering education initiatives that are taking place. Within Australia, there are approximately 18 environmental engineering undergraduate degrees either existing or in the planning stage. The oldest course produced its first graduates in 1992. Most of the courses have been developed from either existing civil engineering or chemical engineering courses, with additional units added to provide a broader base. Because of the way in which the courses have developed, there is sometimes not an overriding philosophy of the achievement of sustainable development, and much of the technology taught still relates to "end-of-pipe" waste treatment rather than cleaner production or pollution prevention.

The environmental engineering courses have the opportunity to produce an environmentally competent engineer with a different attitude to the environment and problem-solving compared to engineers educated within single-discipline courses, either now or in the past. This reflects the new technical culture referred to by Thom (1994).

If the emerging environmental engineering courses do not provide a graduate sufficiently differentiated from the single-discipline product, then the market place is likely to react accordingly and the opportunity to achieve a paradigm shift in engineering practice will have been missed. This must not be allowed to happen and academics have a responsibility to make sure the new graduates meet market demands or, better still, shape them.

Accrediting organisations need to set some framework on which to judge the value of such courses. This should not be prescriptive, but would help those intending to develop such courses.

It would be useful to form a network of environmental engineering academics, preferably linked via electronic mail, to allow exchange of experiences and developments so that we do not keep making the same mistakes and can learn from successful initiatives.

Single-discipline Engineering Degrees

The development of undergraduate environmental engineering courses is partly market driven, but also partly an admission of failure in the environmental education within engineering degrees. This situation has largely occurred because it is difficult to alter existing single-discipline courses to make them environmentally aware. It has been much easier to develop new "marketable" courses clearly labelled as environmental engineering. The question is sometimes asked, does this mean that other engineering courses are not environmental? The answer is often yes, as shown by Codner (1993). There will probably always be many more engineers graduating from single-discipline courses than from environmental engineering courses. Therefore, if we are to change attitudes of new graduates and really move towards sustainability, it is imperative that environmental issues are integrated into single-discipline engineering courses, such as chemical engineering, civil engineering, etc. Within these courses, environmental issues should be integrated into existing course modules, as well as being taught in specialised environmental subjects.

The European Society for Engineering Education (SEFI), which comprises about 250 institutions of higher education, established a working group on environmental engineering in 1991. One of their objectives was the formation of a strong group from universities and industry to raise awareness and stimulate activities in the area of environmental engineering. One of the working group's first activities was to hold a seminar on "Environmental Engineering — A Challenge for Europe" (Vienna, June 1992 (Bahnmuller et al, 1992)). A major theme of the seminar was the introduction of environmental education into engineering courses and the reasons why this was necessary.

Duffell (1993) notes the need for the "greening" of engineering curriculum. He provides an example of a course model on planning and environmental technology developed for civil engineering students. Duffell (1993) also notes the actions of the Institution of Chemical Engineers (UK) in providing environmental guidance to academic institutions seeking degree accreditation. They developed a matrix under three headings — awareness, understanding and in-depth knowledge — through either incorporation in existing studies or enhancement through specific topics.

A study of civil, chemical, mechanical and manufacturing engineering courses at eight Australian universities has shown that they include only a small amount of environmental engineering and technology (Codner, 1993). The chemical, mechanical and manufacturing courses have almost no direct environmental input, although the basic technology is often taught.

The range of environmental engineering subjects in the civil engineering courses studied is from 0% to 17% (Table 1). In some courses, it is possible to bypass environmental subjects altogether. Most of the environmental subjects relate to hydrology and water resources, public health engineering, waste treatment and transport planning. In

Subject Area[1]	Percentage of the Course										
	Melb[2]	Monash[2]	RMIT[2]			UNSW[2]	UTS[2]		Adel-aide[2]	UWA[2]	Curtin[2]
			A	E	P		C	S			
Math/Science	21	19	13	19	13	22	19	19	25	16	12
Traditional Engineering	65	59[3] 70	68	58	65	56 62	57	68	54 69	72 82	70 76
Environmental Eng & Tech.		5 15	5	9	2	8 14	9	2	0 17	0 10	2 8
Inter-disciplinary	9	7	14	14	20	4	8	8	4	2	10
Electives	5	23[4]				4	6	3			

Table 1: *Breakdown of civil engineering courses by subject areas.*

Notes:

1. Subject areas have been broadly defined as:
   - ***Math/Science:*** *includes maths, physics, chemistry, geology;*
   - ***Traditional Engineering:*** *subjects which may be necessary for solving environmental problems, but which are not taught in environmental context, e.g. hydraulics or chemical process engineering;*
   - ***Environmental Engineering & Technology:*** *engineering and science subjects that involve direct environmental topics; e.g. public health engineering, transport planning, environmental impact assessment;*
   - ***Interdisciplinary:*** *usually management, economics, communications, or engineering and society;*
   - ***Electives:*** *free choice of subjects. Choice not usually indicated.*

2. Melb: University of Melbourne; Monash: Monash University, Clayton Campus; RMIT: Royal Melbourne Institute of Technology (A: Asset Management Stream; E: Environmental Management Stream; P: Project Management Stream); UNSW: University of New South Wales; UTS: University of Technology Sydney (C: Civil Stream; S: Structural Stream); Adelaide: University of Adelaide; UWA: University of Western Australia; Curtin: Curtin University.

3. Top figure represents the minimum percentage, and the bottom figure the maximum percentage.

4. Electives have been distributed between traditional and environmental engineering subject areas.

general, the interdisciplinary subjects relate to management, economics and communications. Economics is usually project economics rather than environmental or resource economics. In some cases, it may be possible to take elective subjects in environmental areas. It should be noted that the majority of environmental engineering courses in Australia have developed from civil engineering courses because of their supposed strong environmental direction.

The review of chemical engineering courses is shown in Table 2. The major point to note is the almost total lack of environmental subjects under the definition used in this paper. Traditional engineering subjects account for at least two-thirds of the course. Although many of the courses are concerned with topics related to environmental problems, for example, process engineering, process design, reaction engineering, transport phenomena etc., they do not appear to be applied to environmental problems in a way that the students would recognise. This problem was also noted in electrical engineering at the University of Sydney (Choi and Pudlowski, 1992). Some of this may be overcome in design subjects but, again, this is not obvious. It is necessary to relate subjects like reaction and process engineering to environmental problems within the context of sustainable development. It may be possible to take some of the electives in environmental areas; however, in most cases it appears more likely that they will be in traditional engineering subjects. The concepts of waste prevention and cleaner production receive very little mention. The emphasis is still on efficient "end-of-pipe" treatment.

The review of mechanical and manufacturing engineering courses is shown in Table 3. The range of traditional engineering courses is from 50% to 82%, which is much broader than for either civil or chemical engineering. However, the range does not translate into a larger share of environmental subjects, but into more mathematics and science, and interdisciplinary subjects, which usually relate to accounting and management. The maximum possible environmental content is 6%, with most courses including no subjects that relate directly to the environment. The environmental subjects covered relate to air pollution, environmental noise and energy concepts. The manufacturing courses do not appear to relate to cleaner production, resource management and energy concerns.

Subject Area	Percentage of the Course					
	Melbourne	Monash	RMIT	UNSW	Adelaide	Curtin
Math/Science	32	19	27	29	27	11
Traditional Engineering	67	67	65	60	67 69	85
Environmental Eng & Tech	1		2	1	0 2	
Inter-disciplinary		3	6	1	2	4
Electives		11[1]		9	2	

Table 2: *Breakdown of chemical engineering courses by subject areas.*

Note: 1. Electives have been distributed between traditional and environmental engineering subject areas.

Subject Area	Percentage of the Course									
	Melbourne		Monash	RMIT		UNSW		UTS	Adel-aide	UWA
	Mec	Man	Mec	Mec	Man	Mec	Man	Mec	Mec	Mec
Math/Science	21	21	19	17	11	28	28	15	23	16
Traditional Engineering	69	70	70 / 76	68	74 / 76	50	55	71 / 74	73	82
Environmental Eng & Tech			0 / 6		0 / 2	1	1			
Inter-disciplinary	5	4	5	11	13	6	11	7 / 11	4	2
Electives	5	5	18[1]	4		15	5	3		

Table 3: *Breakdown of mechanical and manufacturing engineering courses by subject areas.*

Note: 1. Electives have been distributed between traditional and environmental engineering subject areas.

The new concepts of sustainable development, waste prevention and minimisation, life-cycle analysis and cleaner production do not appear to have found their way into curricula as yet. Although it is appreciated that some of these ideas are relatively new, it is felt that more action should be taking place to include them in curricula.

Economics related to the environment, rather than simply project management, needs far more attention. This requires consideration of environmental degradation as an economic cost of a project, rather than either an externality, or worse still being ignored and resulting in a cost to the community at some later stage. Sustainability demands inclusion of this topic in course curricula.

Varcoe (1991) has also recognised the need for all engineers to have some environmental education and has devised a single subject called "Engineer and the Environment" for this purpose. In summary, the subject covers:

- the earth as a system;
- engineering life cycles — waste avoidance;
- environmental problems;
- engineering to solve environmental problems;
- environmental law;
- the green scene;
- the role of the media; and
- the role of engineering in ecologically sustainable development.

The University of Sydney has recognised the need for environmental education for electrical engineers and has developed a one-semester subject on environmental issues relating to energy, power generation, electricity distribution, electromagnetic radiation and remote sensing (Choi and Pudlowski, 1992).

Accrediting bodies need to follow the lead of the Institution of Chemical Engineers (UK) and develop guidelines for the inclusion of environmental concepts into existing engineering courses.

Continuing Education

For engineers to take for granted the integration of environmental concerns and sustainability into engineering practice by the year 2010, a major continuing education programme will be necessary for practising engineers who have not been exposed to these issues and concepts in formal engineering degrees. This is an important group, as many are making significant decisions about projects that affect the environment.

Awareness-raising courses will be necessary to develop an understanding of the concepts of sustainability and the need for it to be applied to engineering. However, more detailed courses or seminars will also be necessary to deal with the specific application of sustainability on a sector basis. How will this occur? It is suggested that professional engineering organisations need to take the initiative and provide leadership in this area. The EC/UK is providing leadership in their Code of Professional Practice for engineers and the environment. The Institution of Engineers, Australia is planning to do this through its recently-formed Taskforce on Sustainable Development. However, as noted, it requires an individual or group within such professional organisations to act as a champion for the cause. This will require development of policies on sustainability and environmental guidelines. The WFEO statement on environment and development would be a good place to start, together with the environment policies of the EC/UK and the IEAust. The way will not be easy, as resistance will be met from those who cling to the "old culture", as described by Thom (1993). However, these activities are necessary to achieve attitudinal change, which is necessary to move towards sustainability.

As indicated by Page (1992), there is a need to interact with industry on these issues to determine the specific sectoral needs. Page notes that the University of Cambridge experience is that academic staff often lack experience in key environmental areas such as environmental management, so that it is often necessary to seek industry speakers to deliver significant portions of the course. This interaction can only be beneficial to all concerned — the participants, the university and academic staff, and industry personnel and organisations.

The above relates to awareness-raising and short courses on specific environmental issues. However, there is also a need for graduate courses in environmental engineering to provide high-level technical skills to address particular environmental issues. Universities need to assess their graduate engineering programmes for environmental relevance. Distance education subjects relating to environmental engineering skills should be considered by universities.

The European Polytechnic Environmental Association (EPEA) was established in late 1989 and was approved as a COMETT sectoral University Enterprise Training Programme (UETP) in the field of environmental engineering and management in July 1990. The association has set up an integrated training programme, which includes a one-year, full-time European Masters Programme in Environmental Engineering and a Continuing Education Programme directed at managers and technicians with industrial background (Perona, 1992). The association has recently received support from the EC-TEMPUS Programme to extend its activities to East European countries.

University Enterprise Training Partnership in Environmental Engineering Education (UETP-EEE) Continuing Education and Training Programme (CET) is a goal-oriented course programme that offers modular continuing professional development courses. In addition, the programme supports the training of trainers and delivers training packages to the participants, which can be utilised in distance learning. The organisation has been supporting the creation of a Database of Information on Continuing Engineering Education (DICE), which offers information on courses both in and outside the UETP-EEE programme and allows the planning of individual curricula for environmental studies (Pöyry, 1992).

Conclusion

Sustainability is the way of the future. Our vision should be that by the year 2010, all engineers should adopt and implement the concepts of sustainability as a normal part of their professional activities.

To achieve this vision, a paradigm shift is required on the part of engineers. It is essential to achieve a shift from unsustainable development to sustainable use of the Earth's resources, which will require the linking of development with protection of the environment. The basis for this paradigm shift must be an "attitudinal and behavioural change" by engineers. Change must occur at all levels within the profession, that is, in professional organisations, practising engineers, educators and students. Attitudinal change must be the focus of current activities, for without it the move towards sustainability will not occur.

The vision will not be achieved without considerable effort from professional organisations, education institutions, companies and individuals. The problem is too complex to expect individuals to be able to embrace sustainability and implement the concepts within their own work environment. Professional organisations need to provide a leadership role for the profession in achieving the above vision and moving towards sustainability. IPENZ, IEAust and EC/UK have all started down this road — others need to follow their lead.

Education is considered the key in moving towards sustainability. This will require actions at various levels, such as undergraduate education through environmental engineering degrees and the incorporation of environmental aspects into single-discipline degrees, formal graduate degrees in environmental engineering areas and continuing education for practising engineers. The latter will also involve modules ranging from awareness-raising courses to detailed courses on the implementation of sustainability concepts to specific engineering sectors.

It is recommended that higher education institutions become signatories to the Talloires Declaration. This will help define the corporate environmental philosophy and provide a suitable framework for environmental education and research. It should also allow easier development of environmental initiatives from departments and faculties. "Train the trainer" sessions on environmental awareness-raising and environmental education should also be considered.

Professional engineering organisations also need to provide input into environmental education. This may be through guidelines for environmental engineering courses and the inclusion of environment content into single-discipline courses. All of this must be focused to achieve attitudinal and behavioural change, after which the move towards sustainability will become easier.

It is the responsibility of all engineers to understand and accept the need for sustainability and, hence, the practice of engineering that leads to sustainability. It is unacceptable to say that sustainability is too general a concept that cannot be translated into specific actions. Individuals and organisations not prepared to make the effort to move to sustainability will pay the ultimate price of irrelevancy. Those not prepared to make the change do not have the right to stand in the way of others prepared to make the changes necessary to move to sustainability.

We have the vision. What we need is the resolve and effort to make it happen. Finally, we should all check whether the sun is on our face, and if not, turn towards it.

References

Allen, D (1992). *Survey of Pollution Prevention Education in US Engineering Schools.* Report of the Pollution Prevention Focus Group, Pollution Prevention Education and Training Committee, EPA National Advisory Council for Environmental Policy and Technology. Washington DC: US Government Printing Office.

Bahnmuller, R, M Horvat and I Jansen, eds. (1992). *Environmental Engineering — A Challenge for Europe.* Vienna: SEFI Working Group, Environmental Engineering. 15-16 June 1992.

Carroll, W J (1993). "World Engineering Partnership for Sustainable Development". *ASCE Journal of Issues in Engineering Education and Practice.* 119(3): 238-240.

Choi, Ho Y and Z J Pudlowski (1992). "Environmental Issues and Topics in a Curriculum for Electrical Engineering: New Opportunities and Challenges for Engineering Education". *Proceedings of the 4th Annual Convention and Conference, Australian Association for Engineering Education.* 577-582.

Coates, G H (1993). "Facilitating Sustainable Development: Role of Engineer". *ASCE Journal of Issues in Engineering Education and Practice.* 119(3): 225-229.

Codner, G P (1993). "How Green are Current Curricula?". *Environmental Issues in Engineering Education — Greening Engineering Graduates.* 4th Annual Faculty of Engineering Symposium. University of New South Wales, 22 November 1993. (in print)

Codner, G P, D Huisingh and M Jorgensen (1993). "Environmental Education for Engineers". *Industry and Environment.* 14(4): 23-26.

Cortese, A D (1992). "Education for an Environmentally Sustainable Future". *Environment Science Technology.* 26(6): 1108-1114.

Cortese, A D (1993). "Building the Intellectual Capacity for a Sustainable Future". *Industry and Environment.* 16(4): 6-10.

Disinger, J F (1990). "Environmental Education for Sustainable Development?". *Journal of Environmental Education.* 21(4): 3-6.

Duffell, J R (1993). "Sustainable Development, Engineering Education and Activity". *Engineering Science and Education Journal*. December 1993: 257-265.

Engineering Council (1993). *Code of Professional Practice: Engineers and the Environment*.

Faulkner, J H (1992). "Cleaner Production is Better Business". *UNESCO Nature & Resources*. 28(4): 4-10.

Institution of Engineers, Australia (1989). *Policy on Sustainable Development*. Canberra: IEAust.

Institution of Engineers, Australia (1992). *Environmental Principles for Engineers*. Prepared by the National Committee on Environmental Engineering.

Institution of Professional Engineers of New Zealand (1993). *The Challenge of Sustainable Management of Development and Resources: Discussion Comment*. Prepared by the IPENZ Standing Committee on Engineering and the Environment.

Luthy, R G, D A Bell, J R Hunt, J H Johnson Jr, D F Lawler, C R O'Melia and F G Pohland (1992). "Future Concerns in Environmental Engineering Graduate Education." *ASCE Journal of Issues in Engineering Education and Practice*. 118(4): 361-380.

Page, J (1992). "Environmental Education: A Key Interdisciplinary Subject in Engineering Education". *Environmental Engineering — A Challenge for Europe*. Vienna: SEFI Working Group on Environmental Engineering. 15-16 June: 14-25.

Perona, G (1992). "International Environmental Course Programme COREP". *Environmental Engineering — A Challenge for Europe*. Vienna: SEFI Working Group on Environmental Engineering. 15-16 June: 79-83.

Pöyry, S (1992). "Environmental Engineering in COMETT". *Environmental Engineering — A Challenge for Europe*. Vienna: SEFI Working Group on Environmental Engineering. 15-16 June: 60-63.

Soloviev, E (1992). "A New Dimension in Environmental Education and Training". *Environmental Engineering — A Challenge for Europe*. Vienna: SEFI Working Group on Environmental Engineering. 15-16 June: 44-50.

Thom, D (1994). "The New Technical Culture". *1994 Annual National Engineering Convention*. Melbourne: Institution of Engineers, Australia. NCP 94/3.

Varcoe, J M (1991). "The Environment, Engineering and Education — The Keys to the Future, Broadening Horizons of Engineering Education". *Proceedings of the 3rd Annual Convention and Conference*. Australasian Association for Engineering Education. 400-405.

World Commission on Environment and Development (1987). *Our Common Future*. Oxford: Oxford University Press.

Sustainable Development and Technology

J David Frost

Jennifer DuBose, J David Frost, Jean-Lou A Chameau and Jorge A Vanegas
Center for Sustainable Technology
Georgia Institute of Technology
Atlanta, Georgia, USA

Overview

In the past two decades, environmental issues have gained an increasing amount of attention. It is now *de rigueur* that everything from political policies to commercial products be environmentally "friendly". Major programmes have been initiated to remediate past environmental problems and to ensure that current and future development programmes, activities and technologies are environmentally sensitive.

The emergence of sustainable development is forcing organisations and individuals to re-examine technology and the ways it can be employed to lessen man's impact on the earth. For example, the Department of Defense (DOD) in the United States recognised that environmental concerns need to be integrated into every facet of the military mission, including base operations related to new weapons system development, logistics and disposal. They have initiated an approach to addressing environmental concerns called Conservation, Compliance, Cleanup and Pollution Prevention (C3P2) based on the need for an integrated approach to environmental issues that recognises that there are many ways for DOD to meet its environmental stewardship goals.

Examples such as this indicate the importance of incorporating sustainability ideas into the engineering profession since the work of engineers has such a great impact on the ways that humans interact with nature.

What are the Motivations for Sustainability?

Futurists, science-fiction writers and technological optimists have helped create the vision of a utopian world in which technology is the great panacea. In this idealistic world, technology would enable more work, aimed at satisfying all human needs with less effort. In reality, though, great advances have been made in technology, the most basic of human needs are not close to being universally fulfilled.

For example, technology has not yet solved the problem of poverty. The number of hungry people in the world increased by 56 million, from early 1980s estimates of less than 500 million people to more than 550 million in 1990. There was also an increase in the estimated total number of malnourished children, from 167 million in the early eighties to 188 million in 1990. Ecological impoverishment is also extensive. There are currently an estimated 135 million people living in areas suffering from severe desertification. This poverty does not result from a current lack of resources or a lack of technological know-how, but rather from the failure of policies to use available technology and resources in the best manner possible.

The ability of the planet to renew its stores has also been hampered by the increased population that relies on the earth's resources. The current population growth rate is 1.7 per cent. This means that in 1992, there were 100 million more people on the earth than in 1991. If this rate continues, 3.7 billion people will be added to the planet over the next forty years, and 90 per cent of these people will be born in Africa, Asia or Latin America. Most of this growth will occur in urban areas, making sustainable urban development a critical issue. As of 1990, the world's urban population was 2.4 billion and by the year 2000 this figure is expected to rise to 3.2 billion, with over 70 per cent of these people residing in cities in developing nations. The majority of the poor people in these countries will be living in urban areas, as opposed to rural areas, by the end of this century. In Latin America, it is expected that 90 percent of the poor will be city dwellers by the year 2000.

Although mankind has been exploiting the resources of the earth for approximately two million years, the rate and magnitude of this exploitation has increased in the modern era. The reasons for this are twofold:

- the increase in human population; and

- changes in technology.

Not only are more people using and depleting the earth's resources, but the amount of resources each individual person can access, and thus deplete, has increased because of the availability and attractiveness of technology. Technology has provided a means to extract more resources from the earth, and it often results in returning more waste to the earth. This is due to technologies that have not only facilitated the extraction of more resources than before, but have required the use of more resources. For example, this can be envisaged if one considers energy consumption, which used to be low because of the lack of technology to extract and use large amounts of energy. Technological advances that have improved the quality of life have also resulted in increased usage of large quantities of energy to cool homes and fuel automobiles. To function in an acceptable fashion in many societies today, it is necessary to use, among other things, energy-intensive technologies.

Technology has also brought about the apparent "shrinking" of the world through improved transportation and communication. Today, the earth and the people on it are immensely more interrelated than they were just one hundred years ago. The expansion of the market into the farthest corners of the world has linked distant places together economically, culturally and ecologically. Actions in one part of the globe can have drastic impacts in another, very distant location. Although in the past, these impacts have often been negative, this does not have to be the case. Sharing knowledge among nations can benefit everyone. Increased communication can help solve local problems faster using the experiences of others as a base of knowledge. Greater cooperation can be beneficial to tackling global problems. Technology need not be the enemy of sustainability — it can be utilised to fix some of the problems of the past as well as ensuring future problems are avoided. This can be achieved if a clear perspective of sustainability is formulated and it is made an important and integral part of engineering.

Technologies and policies do not self-manifest, but rather are driven by the desires, goals and values of their designers and developers. Thus, one must not simply look to technology to solve problems, but must look beyond it to the people that create it. Only by educating these individuals of the consequences of non-sustainable approaches and instilling a greater awareness of the benefits of sustainable alternatives can technology be brought to simultaneously address the needs of today and tomorrow. Consequently, it is not difficult to comprehend the overwhelming importance of the engineer in fostering the adoption of sustainability.

The Emergence of Sustainable Development

Recognition of the consequences of a failure to consider and address the motivational factors described above sparked the realisation that the environment and human development are intrinsically linked and led to the eventual formation of the sustainable development movement. Sustainable development can be traced back at least as far as the mid-1960s, when appropriate technology was promoted as the way to help develop the lesser developed countries. Appropriate technology "would take heed of the skill levels of a population, natural resources available indigenously, and pressing social needs defined by the people themselves" (Winner, 1986). Other people have referred to "soft technologies", which are described as:

> *"ecologically sound, small energy input, low or no pollution rate, reversible materials and energy sources only, functional for all time, craft industry, low specialization ... integration with nature, democratic policies, technical boundaries set by nature, local bartering, compatible with local culture, safeguards against misuse, dependent on well-being of other species, innovation regulated by need, steady state economy ..."*

Winner (1986)

By the early 1970s, many people were promoting appropriate technology for the developed world as well. This idea gained recognition and attention alongside the expanding environmental movement of the time.

The idea of environmental assessment and management was introduced for the first time at the 1972 UN Conference on the Human Environment in Stockholm. Even though this conference addressed environmental issues, they were still considered as clearly less important than issues of economic development. Meanwhile, there were indications that the form of economic development would have to be altered. The 1968-74 drought in Ethiopia brought attention to the fact that the environmental costs of traditional economic development might be too high (Stutz, 1993).

All of this debate culminated in the creation of ecodevelopment, or sustainable development, at the UN Environment Program review in 1978, where it was internationally recognised that environmental and development ideas needed to be considered concurrently. The World Conservation Strategy was responsible for the first wide-spread publication of the concept of sustainable development. Acting on this, the UN General Assembly created the World Commission on Environment and Development in 1983 to:

- develop viable proposals for solving major problems related to the environment and development;

- forge ways to increase international cooperation in this area; and

- raise levels of understanding and commitment to the actions of individuals, voluntary organisations, businesses, institutions and governments.

The report titled *Our Common Future*, prepared by the World Commission on Environment and Development (1987) as a result of several years of collaboration by commission members from many different countries, is widely regarded as the seminal text on sustainable development.

What is Sustainable Development?

Sustainable development arose out of the term ecodevelopment. Although Maurice Strong was perhaps the first to use the term "ecodevelopment", it was Ignacy Sachs who took the lead in popularising the idea. He gave this definition in 1974:

> *"A style of development that, in each ecoregion, calls for specific solutions to the particular problems of the region in the light of cultural as well as ecological data and long-term as well as immediate needs."*

Hettne (1990)

There is a shift away from planning only for the immediate future. Ecodevelopment emphasises the need for development programmes that have benefits over the long run and do not purchase prosperity today by sacrificing future well-being. This is not just another kind of development, but a reworking of the concept underlying development. It is no longer possible to think of development in purely economic terms that measure growth by GNP or per capita income.

It is important here to clarify the distinction between growth and development, for they are often mistakenly considered to be interchangeable. The definition of "develop" contains such elements as:

- "to evolve the possibilities of";

- "to make active";

- "to make available or usable"; and

- "to move from the original position to one providing more opportunity for effective use."

In contrast to this, "to grow" is defined very differently:

- "to increase in size by addition of material either by assimilation into the living organism or by accretion in a natural inorganic process."

Growth is about quantity, while development is about quality. In the past when people spoke of development, what was meant was generally "throughput growth", which required ever-increasing quantities of energy and natural resources. This must be replaced by a form of development that is less resource-intensive. "The orthodox view of unlimited economic growth as some kind of natural law must be replaced with a sense of historical relativism." (Hettne, 1990). Growth must stay within the bounds of sustainability, which allows for much less overall growth today than was thought acceptable in the past.

Absolute growth in terms of resource use and waste production cannot continue indefinitely. The planet has a finite store of resources and a limited capacity to accept waste. This has two major implications:

- developing countries will have to find a new way to improve their standards of living; and

- developed countries will have to change their patterns of consumption to allow other countries access to some natural resources.

Instead of following directly in the footsteps of the industrialised nations, developing countries should take advantage of the lessons learned along the way and avoid mistakes made in the past. Although total consumption of resources must be kept at a minimum, this does not mean that the quality of life cannot improve.

Sustainable development encompasses more than just environmental issues. There is also an emphasis placed on developing in a sustainable social context. Social justice is often listed as an integral part of sustainable development and has several forms. Democracy is often considered a prerequisite to making sustainability work; if programmes do not have the support of the community they are unlikely to be successful and are unstable over time. Development programmes and technologies should, as well, be compatible with local culture by respecting the structure of the society and values of the people. Irrespective, there needs to be greater equality in the distribution of resources. This not only has the benefit of reducing conflict between the "haves" and the "have-nots", but also reduces environmental degradation since it is those on either extreme of wealth who most exploit resources.

Since sustainable development incorporates environmental issues that cannot be confined within geopolitical boundaries, it requires enhanced cooperation in the international arena. Not only should national development not come at the cost of injury or harm to people or resources of another country, but development within a particular nation must not infringe upon the abilities of other nations to develop. To avoid the "tragedy of the commons", there must be a mechanism for enforcing this idea, which would entail strengthening the authority of international law. The concerns of developing countries need to be given adequate attention alongside those of the already-developed countries.

Sustainable development does not have a theoretical model that advocates one particular set of actions to develop, as the other major development theories do. Since regions vary by ecosystem type, culture, natural resources and numerous other aspects, it is impossible to prescribe one solution that will work everywhere. This is especially true since sustainability calls for development within the bounds of the local resources and without the destruction of the local culture. There are many paths to development, and each country must choose the one that fits best with their natural and cultural resource base. The Green Revolution is a prime example of why this is important. It tried to create a standardised package of improved variety seeds, irrigation techniques and fertilisers. Although it was somewhat successful in parts of Asia and Latin America, the programme was not successful in Africa. The programme was not designed within the context of these lands and, thus, was not applicable to them. This lesson from agricultural development also applies to urban development. In some cities, transportation needs may be met with buses, whereas a city with a different layout may call for subways. Similarly, sustainable development for one city may entail industrialisation with the appropriate rescues and environmental capacity, but for another city the service sector may offer the best route. It is important to recognise that when one talks about sustainable development, one should recognise that we are working in the context of what has already been done and are not starting from scratch.

Even within a locale, sustainable development will have to be an organic process — "the dimensions of poverty cannot any longer be reduced to only the economic or material conditions of living; the capacity to respond to changes, to change, becomes central." (Gallopin et al., 1989). In *Our Common Future,* the commission stated that significant changes must occur in the structure of societies and in the attitudes and values of the people. This is to be achieved by "vast campaigns of education, debate, and public participation" (World Commission on Environment and Development, 1987). Although many developing nations have become interested in promoting sustainable development, they have not been significant participants in formulating solutions. There needs to be a greater involvement of the local governments if ecodevelopment is going to work. Developed nations have continually dominated world discussions of the issues and have been able to place their concerns high on the agenda.

An important starting point for making these changes is the education of engineers. They will play a key role in the implementation of sustainability since they will design the technologies that will either make or break sustainability. In the past, engineering education has not emphasised sustainability and, thus, for many engineers, it is an afterthought to the design process, if it is thought of at all. By introducing these concepts into the engineering curriculum, it is hoped that sustainability will become an integral part of the design process and sustainable technologies will be a commonplace reality.

References

Dower, N (1992). "Sustainability and the Right to Development". *International Justice and the Third World*. Eds. Robin Attfield and Barry Wilkins. New York: Routledge Publishing.

Gallopin, G C, P Gutman and H Maletta (1989). "Global Impoverishment, Development and Environment". *International Social Science Journal: Reconciling the Sociosphere and the Biosphere*. 121: 375-397.

Goodland, R (1991). "The Case that the World has Reached Limits". *Environmentally Sustainable Economic Development: Building on Brundtland*. Eds. Robert Goodland, Herman Daly, Slah El Serafy and Bernd von Droste. Belgium: UNESCO.

Hettne, B (1990). *Development Theory and the Three Worlds*. New York: John Wiley & Sons.

Pezzey, J (1989). *Definitions of Sustainability*. University of Colorado.

Stutz, B (1993). "The Landscape of Hunger". *Audubon*. March-April 1993.

Tolba, M (1982). *Development Without Destruction: Evolving Environmental Perceptions*. Dublin: Tycooly International Publishing.

Tudela, F (1992). *Toward a New International Pact for Sustainable Development: Latin America and Caribbean Viewpoints*. Washington DC: InterAmerican Development Bank.

United Nations Development Program (1991). *Cities, People & Poverty: Urban Development Cooperation for the 1990s*. New York: UNDP.

Winner, L (1986). *The Whale and the Reactor: A Search for Limits in an Age of High Technology*. Chicago: University of Chicago Press.

World Commission on Environment and Development (1987). *Our Common Future*. Oxford: Oxford University Press.

APPENDIX

Sustainable Development and Technology Synthesis of Issues Discussed in Workshop Presentation

It is intended that this appendix acts as a stimulus for workshop discussion. Issues raised by the concept of sustainability as applied to engineering technology are raised in point form. These are prefaced by a listing of issues associated with the sustainability concept itself.

Sustainability Issues

- environmental protection and restoration;

- depletion of natural resources;

- population growth;

- local equity;

- global equity;

- quality of life;

- reality vs perception;

- global vs local;

- socio-political environment; and

- technology.

Definitions of Sustainability

World Commission on Environment and Development (1987)
"Development that meets the needs of the present without compromising the ability of future generations to meet their own needs."

UNDP Hague Report
For some "all future economic growth must stop", others "are disdainful of any natural limits to continued growth and place their faith in technological fixes" and some "foresee a major conflict in the interests of the North and the South".

Other Definitions
- conservation of natural resources;

- environmental quality and protection;

- ecological/holistic world view?;

- economical vs ethical ideal;

- sustainability of life vs sustainability of privileges;

- substitutability — acceptable and how much?;

- cultural and social stability;

- poverty reduction;

- population growth?;

- global — will remain vague;

- regional and local — progress will be made;

- equity — political and public will?;

- environment — significant progress will be made; and

- development — larger role for quality of life.

Sustainability: An Engineer's Viewpoint

Economic growth that is in harmony with the environment and related to improvements in quality of life. Sustainable technology is the finding of practical solutions to help achieve this goal.

- Maximising natural economics, effectiveness and efficiency

    — development as a compatible part of the Earth's systems;

    — emulating nature in the production and use of resources; and

    — removing barriers to human goodwill, cooperation and capacity enhancement.

- attaining necessary balance;

    — resource accessibility;

    — requirements of communities; and

    — capacity of communities to meet their requirements.

- Implementing guidance principles to meet the effectiveness, efficiency and balance requirements of communities.

Sustainable Technologies

Major Categories
- Resource preservation

    — appropriate technologies;

    — recycle technologies; and

    — high efficiency energy production, transmission and use.

- Renewable energy utilisation

    — solar energy;

— wind energy;

— geothermal energy;

— hydroelectric energy;

— biomass energy.

• Pollution prevention

— chemical selectivity (minimise by-products);

— CFC replacement; and

— chemical reformulation.

Examples of Sustainable Technology

SaskPower's Shand Power Station is the first commercial plant to use a limestone injection system that captures acid rain-causing sulphur dioxide before it enters the atmosphere.

Molten Metal Technology is currently commercialising a patented, revolutionary recycling technology — catalytic extraction processing (CEP). It will revert hazardous wastes to its elements and then combine these elements into industrial inputs.

Researchers working in Canada and Bangladesh have developed a chemical additive to improve a key step in the processing of jute, a plant that provides an economic mainstay for many southern Asian countries. With this enzyme process, time is decreased and high-quality fibers can be extracted from the jute that was once considered waste.

Chrysler Corporation reduced the amount of paint used on cars by 50% while also reducing the resultant air emissions by 70%. In 1994, all of their new vehicles will have CFC-free airconditioning units.

The Advanced Integrated Wastewater Pond Systems (AIWPS) offer a sustainable means of pollution prevention by reducing the generation of biosolids and the associated risks to human health and environmental integrity. Biosolids are virtually eliminated without the separate processing and disposal inherent in conventional methods.

Thermco is becoming well-known for its Terminator technology, an internal secondary condenser for air conditioning and refrigeration systems. Thermco-run systems can cut the use of ozone-depleting CFCs by 50%, energy requirements by 25% and maintenance costs by 20%.

DEJA SHOE will manufacture and market footwear made from recycled materials, as well as ecologically-obtained plant materials, and develop new technologies, uses and markets for these materials.

Anthony Convery has developed a machine for recycling waste concrete from ready-mix trucks and on-site concrete mixers. The machine, which is now selling worldwide, separates sand, aggregate, cement and liquid from the waste concrete, enabling the materials to be reused in future mixes.

Appropriate Technology and Community Environment (APACE) has developed affordable and readily maintainable micro-hydro electric power generating schemes, which can be installed at low cost with assistance from village communities and thereafter maintained by them.

The Rhone-Poulenc company in France has developed a process that neutralises wastes produced in the synthesis of vitamin B12. The treatment of these highly pollutant wastes produces a residue, which can be used as fertiliser.

Research is being conducted at the University of California, Berkeley to redesign ponds for waste management. Paddle-wheel mixed algal growth ponds are cost-effective for wastewater oxidation and efficient in fixing solar energy and in reclaiming water nutrients and energy from organic wastes.

Venture Victoria USA engineers have announced a fully-integrated electronic system that combines and controls a natural gas-diesel mixture to maximise fuel efficiency and reduce emissions of heavy diesel engines. Extensive testing shows a cut in CO_2 emissions by up to 15%, NO_x by up to 25% and smoke by up to 80%.

A single-use disposable camera from Kodak is recycled ("100%" closed materials loop) into new cameras after use.

Sustainable Technology: Current Research Areas

- Chemical industry — environmentally-benign processes

    — supercritical spray of paints;

    — electrolytic steelmaking;

    — alternative synthesis of sulfolane;

    — replacement of CFC-based cleaners of printed wiring;

    — limited by-product chemistry; and

    — environmentally benign solvents for chemical, petrochemical and pharmaceutical processes.

- Transportation

    — alternative-fueled modes of transport;

    — fast-charging battery technology;

    — alternative community living patterns;

    — neotraditional community design;

    — transportation technologies for developing countries;

    — material recycling; and

    — composite/new materials.

- Public policy

    — economic incentives and constraints;

    — social policy and ethics; and

— negotiation and conflict resolution.
- Manufacturing
  — design for disassembly and recycling; and
  — component interchangeability.
- Water supply and management
  — integrated water resources system management;
  — global warming and water resources; and
  — hydrological flows and biochemical processes.
- Energy
  — solar power, photovoltaics;
  — pulsed combustion;
  — waste pyrolysis systems;
  — waste to energy conversion;
  — gasification and wet thermal oxidation; and
  — coal 2000 programme.
- Environmental remediation
  — low-energy and engineering bioremediation;
  — anaerobic biotechnology optimisation;
  — cyanobacterial mats; and
  — mobile air emissions and sustainable metropolitan environments.
- Infrastructure
  — plastics and composites for rehabilitation; and
  — polymer and recycled "plastic bridges".
- Construction/Architecture
  — prefab materials for solid waste reduction;
  — recyclable forming;
  — life-cycle analysis;
  — enviro-sensitive specifications using hypermedia;
  — energy efficiency and conservation;
  — "cyclic city"; and
  — affordable housing.

Sustainability: Measures

- Issues

  —objective language of sustainability;

  —entire life-cycle to be considered;

  —global vs local;

  —project is part of larger system;

  —optimise the whole system;

  —different ecosystems: different metrics;

  —conflicting goals, acceptable trade-offs; and

  —cost: "price" reflects "true" cost.

- 1995 Conference on Metrics and Research Needs for Sustainability, Georgia Tech.

Sustainability: Education

- Generation responsible for solving problems less educated than previous generations?

- Discrepancy between issues and public perception.

- 75% of the world's population has only 15% of the world's engineers and scientists.

- Education of women.

- "Retrofitting" (or re-education) of professionals.

- Environmentally-conscious engineers.

Continuing Engineering Education

Ms Sirkka Pöyry
The Finnish Association of Graduate Engineers
TEK
Helsinki, Finland

"The European Community's study of skills needs linked to the environment, points to the diffusion of environmental considerations across a very wide range of economic activities. This will bring about great changes in product and production processes. Environmental skills need to become generic skills, and will be required across a range of occupations and skills levels. The relationships between products, production methods, and social and ecological infrastructure at all levels — local, regional and global — will need to be understood. For example, management training will combine business administration with technological and environmental awareness."

"There is need for managers and engineers to consider the whole process of design and manufacture as an integrated system."

Commission of the European Communities (1994)

The statements above illustrate the European guidelines for training and education. Continuous education and lifelong learning are the tools that will bring about competitiveness and sustainable development and are concepts upon which the European education policy will be based.

Environmental Skills in Demand

As we approach the 21st century, the sustainability of traditional approaches to economic growth, production and consumption are in question. Global awareness of environmental problems and the need to respond to the new environmental demands when applying technology are increasing. Many enterprises regard already-clean technologies and practices as a matter of survival and part of the business, and cost is not the only factor. While profits remain the priority, enterprises now see it in their best interest to have environmentally-sound products and processes.

Developments in our society, particularly increasing urbanisation and industrialisation throughout the world, is accelerating environmental problems. In some of our old European cities, like London, we have already seen that improvement is possible. In developing countries, this process of urbanisation and industrialisation has only just started, and rapid population growth combined with poor economies often lead to slums close to big cities, with poor hygiene, poor water quality and inadequate waste management, if it exists at all.

We can take China as an example of the future challenges. Today, the population of China is about 1.2 billion, and 20 per cent of them, i.e. about 240 million, are living in cities. In 30 to 50 years, about 30,000 townships are going to become cities and the urban population will be 60% to 70%. It means increasing social problems and unemployment, housing shortages, energy problems and an enormous growth in the number of cars, and the associated traffic problems, waste management problems and waste water treatment problems.

The rapid development of many newly-industrialised countries provides new challenges for engineering skills. When building new industrial plants or exploiting new energy resources, the environmental impacts must be considered. Short-term profits should not be allowed to destroy long-term welfare. New technologies are needed to avoid the environmental mistakes made in the early years of western industrial growth.

If we want to build our future and the future of our children upon the principle of sustainable development, it is not enough to clean up the pollution or to protect nature with tree-planting and afforestation programmes. All that is very important, and those programmes raise peoples' awareness and encourage them to act responsibly, but if we want to have an improvement in the long run, we have to learn to prevent pollution, minimise the environmental impact of our activities and change our patterns of planning and consumption. In this, engineers have key roles.

New Concepts are Needed
Initial engineering education must be supported by continuing education and training that responds to industry's and society's specified environmental demands.

In this context, Environmental EuroPro, a system for professional development in environmental engineering, is introduced. This programme is an example of goal-oriented continuing education, with an individual study plan developed by the student, his or her employer and a university. EuroPro promises to provide the environmental training needed to meet the environmental challenges of today and tomorrow.

A new phenomenon in western society is a high unemployment rate, even among graduated engineers. Re-employment is often possible only through retraining. Up-to-date knowledge is needed — the increasing needs of environmental skills open new possibilities.

The Changing Role of Engineers
The professional profile of engineers has changed over recent decades. The engineer is a problem solver, and the diversity of problems that require his/her consideration has increased. Before, the problems were defined simply in technological and, sometimes, in economic terms. Today, staggering population growth, increasing standards of living and demands for energy and natural resources have intensified the conflict in our relationship with the natural environment. Awareness of limited natural resources and the environmental impact of human activity has become a major issue for governments, industry and education, and it is placing serious new demands and challenges on engineers.

New challenges surface when legislation and society's expectations set new demands on enterprises:

- environmental auditing (a systematic investigation of the environmental impact and implementation of all activities in an enterprise) is already becoming obligatory;

- international agreements require continuous monitoring and increasingly stringent control of emissions;

- environmental impact assessment is demanded when planning new development projects; and

- life-cycle assessment has become a useful tool for evaluating the environmental impact of products.

These developments create the need for every engineer to have knowledge of environmental issues and the impacts related to his own field of technology. But how many of our current engineers are trained to respond to these challenges?

Industry is well aware of the changes in society and, especially, in the demands of their customers. Many companies now regard environmentally sound approaches as a competitive factor or even as a matter of survival. In addition, environmental technology is one of the fastest growing markets in many western countries, and so industry is looking to take advantage of new business opportunities. In many countries, however, a current lack of well-educated and trained environmental engineers is hindering the realisation of the potential in these areas.

Continuing Education Responds to Rapid Changes

Environmental programmes are under development in many universities. In Europe, discussion of environmental engineering curricula and society's and industry's needs has been going on for several years.

Close links and active cooperation between higher education institutions and industry are needed. However, universities should not expect industry to provide the wisdom and long-term visions for education. Typically, industry's planning is on a short-term basis compared with universities' planning. The results of changes in initial university education begin to take effect in industrial practice after approximately ten years, whereas industry normally expects a return on investment within only a couple of years. If we are looking for immediate changes, a well-developed continuing engineering education programme is the only way to offer flexible solutions and rapid responses to the growing demand for new knowledge.

According to our investigations of industry's skills needs, it seems clear that industry appreciates newly-graduated engineers with good basic knowledge in science, technology and ecology. These engineers are expected to be particularly strong in their own technological field, and they should graduate at a relatively young age.

Many representatives from industry are of the opinion that an engineer who has gained good theoretical knowledge in science, physics, chemistry, ecology and technology will easily learn all the special knowledge needed for each individual job. Many enterprises prefer to employ young engineers and complete their training on-the-job or in different continuing education programmes.

However, throughout an engineer's education, environmental aspects should be integrated with technical studies. An engineer should learn to consider the environmental impact of technological applications in the same way he must consider technical functioning and safety or economic feasibility. If an engineer does not learn the importance of considering the environment during his/her studies, it will be very difficult to build up environmental special skills in continuing education.

Specialist courses in environmental topics are often recommended as the last part of engineering studies or in postgraduate studies. If an engineer is specialising too early in a narrow field, it will be harder for him/her to find a job in industry. The range of appropriate employment possibilities will be very limited. This is also a danger when an engineer is educated in environmental matters in an early phase of his/her studies, as the specialist topics often push the basics aside. After broad-based initial education and industrial experience, specialisation can be developed as the career progresses. Thus, there are better opportunities for bringing the interdisciplinary nature of environmental issues into the study programme.

In addition to the mainstream path of education and career in the industry, there is still a need in society for a number of environmental generalists, especially in municipal offices. Therefore, special courses or curricula for environmental engineers are also needed. A variety of different choices in engineering education are needed and a standard recommendation for an ideal education is not necessary. But the variety in initial education places demands on continuing education.

Often in continuing education programmes, the background of the students varies extensively, as does the extent of their knowledge. These variations should be used to enhance the richness of the courses and the learning process. New methodologies, exchange of ideas and interactive participation programmes are needed, and the main emphasis should be on how to consider the individual needs of the student and his/her employer. Individual paths and self-study elements, individual projects and exercises are needed.

International Cooperation

Environmental pollution does not recognise state borders. Rivers flow from one country to another, carrying their pollution to the sea. The winds do not obey any human rulers when they transport emissions from human activities through the air. The problems have changed from local to global. This means that environmental solutions must be internationally developed and implemented — we need international contacts and cooperation when regulating industrial processes and transport and in setting limits for emissions and pollution. We also need international cooperation in education and training. Knowledge needs to be transferred as soon as possible from research to practical applications. We need the best available technologies for our environment's sake.

Several different models for international collaboration have been identified:

- researcher education;

- university-enterprise collaboration;

- summer universities;

- international organisations' activities; and

• east-west and north-south university collaboration.

The list of tools employed in collaboration is also long: PhD programmes, researcher course programmes, student courses, student exchange, student placements in industry, expert exchange, training educators activities, workshops and conferences, surveys and inventories and various working groups.

The International Association for Continuing Engineering Education (IACEE) is one of the worldwide networks that offers its members an excellent forum for discussions and information exchange.

Regional societies also play an important role. In Europe, the European Society for Engineering Education (SEFI) established a working group on environmental engineering in 1991. The operational procedures of the working group are annual seminars, working group meetings at the annual SEFI conference and publications. The topic of the 1993 annual seminar was cleaner technology, with an emphasis on industrial practice and integration of the concept in university programmes. In April 1994, the working group organised a seminar on sustainability and engineering education.

Strategies to focus training activities in specific areas and to disseminate this knowledge are needed. The "train-the-trainer" concept is employed by many international networks to achieve this goal. Another way to optimise the use of resources is cooperation with other organisations by collecting information and disseminating training materials.

The UNEP (United Nations Environment Programme) working group on education is producing an inventory of cleaner production education and training resources in cooperation with the UETP-EEE. This inventory will include education and continuing education courses and educators in universities and major institutions. The inventory will focus on:

• university courses and distance learning courses;

• university curricula;

• educational materials;

• planning and organisation of educational programmes in cleaner production; and

• affiliations with international organisations.

The inventory will be presented as reports that describe good concepts for courses and curricula, lists of available educational materials and multiple indices.

European Programmes

In Europe, the European Community's research, education and training programmes have increased the level of international collaboration remarkably. During the last few years, the environmental sector has become increasingly active within the framework of these programmes. It has become the largest field, for example, in the Community Programme for Education and Training in Technology (COMETT).

The University-Enterprise Training Partnership in Environmental Engineering Education (UETP-EEE) was established in 1990 as a project under the COMETT programme.

The main emphasis of the UETP-EEE's activities is on continuing education and university-enterprise cooperation (Poje and Pöyry, 1991,1992; Stene, 1991).

The aim of UETP-EEE is to increase environmental awareness and to assist those working in the field of technology to develop and implement cleaner technologies and cooperate in moving towards sustainable development. UETP-EEE is a European network of over 50 organisations, universities and enterprises and engineering and industrial associations from different European countries. It has also strong links with many international organisations.

The main objectives and actions are to:

- enhance cooperation between universities and enterprises and improve exchange of information by the provision of an effective information network;

- determine the training needs of industry, including small- and medium-sized enterprises (SMEs), by conducting surveys of existing environmental engineering provision and future requirements and skills needs;

- provide training for industry by the development of continuing education and training programmes;

- assist university and enterprise trainers to develop new approaches to environmental engineering by providing workshops and symposia; and

- foster European cooperation and development of human resources in the field of environmental engineering by student placements and expert exchanges (fellowships) and other international cooperation activities.

The expert exchange programme has proved to be extremely successful because of its wide circulation. The exchange often leads to permanent cooperation between participating organisations. All individuals participating in the programme for expert exchange are trained. Exchanges always involve one partner from a university and the other from industry. Fellowships vary from two to 12 months. Economic support is limited to the direct and indirect mobility costs of the fellowships.

The programme for student traineeships provides placements and grants to enable students studying environmental issues and technology at a higher education institution in one European country to take up a period of employment in an enterprise in another European country.

UETP-EEE also provides a programme for continuing engineering education and produces learning materials. It organises an annual education development conference called ENTREE (Environmental Training in Engineering Education). The idea is to facilitate communication for transfer of research results from universities and research institutes via training to industrial applications. The conference programme consists of lectures, discussions, presentations of scientific papers and visits to institutes and enterprises.

EuroPro — a European Strategy for Goal-oriented Continuing Education

EuroPro was developed to serve European industry, as a measure for improving competitiveness and matching skills development with individual and industrial needs.

Over the past few years, EuroPro has successfully created a European strategy for professional development in the oil and chemical industries. Companies in the chemical and process industries have found EuroPro effective in developing their core technological competencies through continuing education studies that meet the requirements of both companies and individuals. Interested companies work with their employees, together with a European university, to develop a curriculum that matches the needs and goals of the individual.

One of the major advantages of the EuroPro concept is its flexibility. EuroPro makes it easier to include a professional development programme in corporate strategy. Courses can be chosen from a variety of different sources in different countries to form an individual study plan, which must be accredited by the EuroPro Board. Project work and on-the-job training are an important part of the studies. For engineers, the professional qualification they receive brings flexibility to their career paths and high-added European value to their skills.

The first EuroPro degrees, focused on chemical and oil companies, have been completed, and the students' feedback has been encouraging. However, an attractive feature of EuroPro is its adaptability to various technological fields.

Following the model's successful implementation in the oil and chemical industries, UETP-EEE is establishing an adaptation of EuroPro that focuses on environmental engineering. Market research conducted by UETP-EEE has indicated a large demand for training in environmentally-oriented SMEs and in municipal offices (Kauranen, 1991). However, the financial and human resources often set tight limits. New, flexible solutions are needed.

When adapting EuroPro to the environmental sector, target markets are very different than they were with the process industries. Environmental continuing education is needed in a variety of different enterprises. Oil and chemical industries consist mainly of large, international companies, but environmental knowledge is needed in every company, big and small, as well as in government offices and municipalities. Environmental education and training is not a homogeneous market.

Environmentally-oriented SMEs in Finland, Norway and the United Kingdom emphasised the value of a modular structure because they cannot afford to send their staff to courses for a longer period. They appreciate individual development programmes tailored to meet the needs of the enterprise. Similar results were reported in the analysis of the environmental sector of COMETT conducted by UETP-EEE in 1992 (Pöyry and Miettinen, 1992). A systematic and goal-oriented approach to postgraduate training was seen as more effective than an extensive variety of ad-hoc courses from random course providers. That is exactly what we offer with the EuroPro Programme.

The previous startup module for oil and chemical industries dealt with cleaner production, and among the participants there were already some new students outside of the oil and chemical industries. The next startup module for new students will be in October 1994 in Brussels with the theme of "Environmental Impact Assessment". A majority of the students will come from municipalities from several European countries and it can be regarded as a new, successful extension to the EuroPro programme.

Re-employment as a Training Challenge

Europe and most western countries have for several years suffered serious recession. The process of industrial restructuring and adaptation has accelerated, many traditional industries have left the market and unemployment figures have been at a record high. In this period of change, the European Union strongly emphasises in its policy the importance of job creation, competitiveness and cohesion.

> *"As a consequence of the massive changes which can be expected, the skills of Europe's labour force need to be continually updated so as to avoid social exclusion and high economic and social costs. To this end, education, training and retraining should be a priority investment,"*

Commission of the European Communities (1994).

Continuing education programmes as a retraining tool for university graduated engineers, threatened by unemployment, have been a new challenge. UETP-EEE, together with the Helsinki University of Technology, has developed a six- to seven-month course programme in the environmental field, called "Environment is a Business Idea".

The experimental course will start in September 1994. The students will be selected with tests in order to measure their motivation and background knowledge. Language skills will be emphasised because part of the teaching will be in English, and individual projects and training periods can be implemented abroad. The majority of the participants will be university graduate engineers (MSc) with several years experience in different fields.

The first two weeks of the course consist of preparatory modules, including information searching and handling, computer programs, project management, communications and language skills. The environmental modules during the following three months are on:

• European and international environmental policy, legislation and regulations;

• basic courses in monitoring air pollution, water and wastewater treatment, soil quality and groundwaters, noise control;

• energy and environment;

• risk management;

• environmental and quality management; and

• environmental auditing and life-cycle assessment.

Three months is a very short time to cover such a variety of topics. Therefore, it is desirable that the participants will individually choose certain topics on which to concentrate and receive in-depth knowledge. Because of the self-study and project periods, it is possible, to a certain extent, to individualise the course programme. The enterprises will have an important part in the planning and implementation of the course. They offer the participants training possibilities in their industrial projects at home and abroad. Practical on-the-job training is scheduled to last three months.

During the course, continuous evaluation of teaching methods, the different learning materials and learning results will be implemented. The main goal of the course is that at the end a majority of the participants will be re-employed by an enterprise or self-employed as expert consultants.

References

Commission of the European Communities (1994). *Skills for Competitive and Cohesive Europe — A Human Resources Outlook for the 1990s.* Brussels: Commission of the European Communities.

Kauranen, K (1991). *Knowledge is the Key to Success — A Study of the Environmental Training Needs of SMEs.* Helsinki: UETP-EEE.

Industrial Research and Advisory Committee of the European Commission (1994). *Quality and Relevance — the Challenge to European Education.* Brussels: Industrial Research and Advisory Committee of the European Commission.

Poje and S Pöyry, eds. (1991,1992). *Proceedings ENTREE 91-92 Environmental Training in Engineering Education.* Helsinki: UETP-EEE.

Pöyry, S and P Miettinen (1992). *Analysis of the Environmental Sector of COMETT.* Helsinki: UETP-EEE.

Saari, P (1990). *Ympäristönsuojelun opetus teknillisissä tiedekunnissa ja korkeakouluissa* (Environmental Education in Technical Universities and Technical Faculties in Finland). Helsinki: TEK. Finnish.

Stene, V (1991). *Training is the Key to Knowledge — the Key to Success.* Oslo: UETP-EEE.

General Papers

Course Design in Environmental Engineering: The Advantage of Hindsight

David L Wilkinson
Department of Civil Engineering
University of Canterbury, New Zealand
(formerly School of Civil Engineering,
University of New South Wales, Australia)

Engineering and Environmentalism

Public awareness and concern for the impact of human activity on the environment is a relatively recent phenomenon and one that is evolving rapidly. Rachel Carson's book "Silent Spring", published in 1963, was one of the first expressions of concern addressed at the general public. Carson died the following year and so never saw the worldwide growth of the popular movement she helped to inspire.

Engineering at that time was almost totally concerned with technical issues; it was engineers who designed and constructed urban freeways and nuclear power stations; it was they who had sent men into orbit around the earth and five years later around the moon.

On the other side of the coin, engineers were involved in the dumping of mercury-containing wastes into Minamata Bay, Japan, resulting in 800 deaths from mercury poisoning. Nuclear accidents at Windscale, and later at Three Mile Island and Chernobyl, eroded public confidence in the integrity of the profession and the often reactive and defensive response of engineers has done little to allay those fears.

The activities of environmental activists has developed a broad-based public concern for the environment and this has resulted in the enactment of environment legislation that impacts on many engineering activities. While some engineers have been pro-active in regards to the environmental impact of engineering works, it would be true to say that many engineers are uncomfortable with the new responsibility they must bear. It is not generally appreciated by the community that engineers are public servants in the truest sense of the word. Engineers design, construct and manage the infrastructure that provides the comforts the community takes for granted in the developed countries: electricity, communications, transport, water, sanitation — all the basics of modern life. It is ironic that as a whole engineers are not regarded as the "good guys". This, I believe, is largely due to a reluctance among many engineers to deal with nontechnical issues, coupled with a lack of communication skills, which has led to the perception in the community that engineering activities are necessarily harmful to the environment.

The Emergence of Environmental Engineering

Environmental legislation enacted over the past 25 years has obliged engineers to be increasingly aware of the effects of their activities on the environment. Practices that were acceptable in the past are no longer acceptable. But there is still a long way to go. In 1985, the Environmental Engineering Division of the American Society of Civil Engineers published the following statement of purpose:

> *"Environmental engineering is manifest by sound engineering thought and practice in the solution of problems of environmental sanitation, notably in the provision of safe palatable, and ample public water supplies; the proper disposal or recycle of waste water and solid wastes; the adequate drainage of urban and rural areas for proper sanitation; and the control of water, soil and atmospheric pollution and the social and environmental impact of these solutions."*

The response of a true technocrat. The statement is full of technological detail, but there is no mention of sustainability, environmental management, the assessment of risk and the role of the public in environmental decision making.

If environmental engineers are to have a significant role in environmental decision making, they must be more than mere technocrats to be dragged out when there is a need for numbers to be crunched so that other professionals can make the real decisions. Engineers are trained to solve multifaceted problems, assess risk and make decisions based on limited information, precisely the type of problems that are encountered in environmental decision making and the development of environmental policy. The contribution engineers can make in these areas is yet to be fully realised.

Environmental Engineering Programme Requirements

Environmental engineering is highly multidisciplinary and ideally requires skills in a number of disciplines. A by no means exhaustive list might include:

- from the physical sciences

    — mathematics;

    — physics;

    — chemistry;

    — geology.

- from the biological sciences

    — biology;

    — microbiology;

    — ecology.

- from civil engineering

    — mechanics;

    — water engineering;

    — geotechnical engineering;

    — public health engineering;

    — waste management.

- from chemical engineering

    — mass transfer and material balance;

— unit operations;

— fluid/solid separation.

- from environmental studies

  — environmentalism;

  — environmental processes;

  — urban planning and design;

  — environmental impact assessment.

- others

  — communications;

  — remote sensing;

  — economics;

  — ethics;

  — law.

In addition, it is particularly important for environmental engineers to be conversant with risk analysis and systems modelling and have well-developed communication skills. It is also highly desirable that students have the opportunity to practice these skills in an integrated fashion before graduating, as it is this integrated multidisciplinary approach that characterises environmental engineering.

It is clear that it is not possible to provide a comprehensive coverage of all of the above topics in a four-year undergraduate programme. Is it possible, then, to adequately train an environmental engineer without exposing him or her to this daunting mass of material? The answer is yes, but in doing so it is crucial to identify the qualities that can only be effectively learned in a university environment and those that can be learned on the job. In other words, at university the emphasis should be on the development of concepts rather than the rote learning of procedures. These are best learned through application in the workplace. The content of environmental engineering courses is not a decision for academics alone, but should be made in conjunction with the users of the services of environmental engineers. And this is not simply their prospective employers. Nepotism of this form fails to recognise that environmental engineers need to work closely with the community and with other professions. Its only sensible that these groups have some input into the training of environmental engineers.

Programmes tend to be largely taught by staff from the core discipline, usually civil or chemical engineering, and courses tend to strongly reflect the interests of the core area. Consequently, the syllabi cover only a limited number of the subjects listed above. This is not necessarily bad in that environmental engineering covers a broad range of areas and some degree of specialisation is inevitable. Nevertheless, it is vital to identify those components that are particularly important for environmental engineers and to ensure that they are included.

There are two topics listed above that I view as particularly important for environmental engineers, but which because of their less technical nature, tend to be regarded as of secondary importance, if not omitted altogether from many courses. They are:

- Environmentalism — environmental engineers need to have an appreciation of the range of attitudes towards environmental issues within society, the "spectrum of environmentalism" as it has been phrased by O'Riordan, if they are to effectively serve the community. An understanding of the emergence of the environmental movement and the role of the principal environmental organisations is also necessary if engineers are to have credibility with the various environmental interest groups, who often act as spokespersons for the community.

- Communication skills — to be able to communicate clearly and effectively is important for any engineer, but particularly so for environmental engineers who work in a highly multidisciplinary environment and who are frequently involved with public interest groups in often contentious and sometimes hostile situations. They also need to be able to communicate effectively with specialists from other disciplines and to coordinate and interpret their activities.

Integration in Environmental Engineering Programmes

While the above may reflect some ideal, the reality is that this ideal is seldom realised. Most environmental engineering programmes have developed out of existing engineering programmes, either civil or chemical engineering, or in a few instances from environmental science/studies programmes. Subjects in the programme that are not traditionally taught in the core programme are usually provided on a servicing basis by other departments. The desirability of this is questionable given the high level of interdisciplinary contact in the practice of environmental engineering. Because of the number of topics that fall into this category, there is a risk that courses will develop into a series of essentially disconnected parts.

It could, therefore, be argued that environmental engineering is best taught by a single school or department, thereby maximising contact between staff involved in teaching the programme and providing the best opportunities for course integration. For example, a biologist teaching ecology to a class of environmental engineers needs to appreciate how those students are going to utilise that material in their later professional lives. This understanding is facilitated if the biologist works in an environmental engineering department.

It can equally well be argued that specialists are best housed with people working in the same field, and proceeding with our example, the biologist working in an environmental engineering department may lose touch with developments in his or her own field.

The essential issue is not really where teachers of an environmental engineering course are housed, but how well they interact. An effective course will be one where staff interaction is facilitated and actively encouraged. Many opportunities exist for collaboration in the classroom, in research and consulting. However, this is unlikely to occur on a significant scale unless the opportunities are created. It requires commitment and drive within the core institution and the necessary support and infrastructure.

The Future

Social and environmental issues are playing an increasingly important role in the work of engineers. The demand for engineers with an understanding of these issues and an ability to communicate effectively in both technical and nontechnical language will continue to increase. The engineering paradigm is in a state of evolution and the new environmental engineers are at the forefront of this change. The long-term benefactors are both the community and the profession.

Acknowledgements

The writer had the privilege of chairing the committee that led to the establishment of Bachelor and Masters programmes in Environmental Engineering at the University of New South Wales in 1991 and 1992 respectively. Many colleagues from academia, government, industry and consulting contributed to the planning of the programme, but I would particularly like to thank Robin Fell, Ronny Harding, Stephen Moore and Mark Wainwright for their valued and significant contributions. The views expressed here are my own and do not necessarily reflect those of the above.

Training Environmental Engineers at Tertiary Level: An Asia-Pacific Perspective

John E Hay

Coordinator of the UNEP Network for Environmental Training
at Tertiary Level in Asia and the Pacific (NETTLAP)
and
Environmental Science, University of Auckland
Auckland, New Zealand

Abstract

Through their involvement in industry, construction and numerous other activities, engineers have the potential to impose significant impacts on the environment. Whether these impacts are beneficial or detrimental is largely dependent on the attitudes, knowledge and skills of the engineers. Hence, engineers are very important targets for environmental education and training.

Numerous writers have noted the need for a paradigm shift with respect to the training of engineers, with emphasis on a multidisciplinary approach that incorporates social, economic, political and legal perspectives in addition to those of the natural sciences. Training should also develop communication skills and an ability to consult with, and reflect the attitudes and needs of, diverse groups.

Nowhere but in the Asia-Pacific region is the requirement for environmentally astute engineers greater. The region contains over half of the world's population. Both population and economic growth rates are high, as is the rate of urbanisation. These and other factors are placing unprecedented pressure on the environment and natural resources. Undoubtedly, the need to harmonise the goals of environmental protection, resource conservation, economic growth and social progress is at its greatest in the Asia-Pacific region, but so too are the challenges that defy fulfilment of these wants.

A variety of influences and imperatives are determining the approach to and content of environmental training in the region. Decentralised, flexible approaches are required in order to accommodate the diversity of the region and ensure local ownership of the process. Similarly, training methods must adapt to allow incorporation of traditional knowledge and practices and foster political and cultural sensitivity. The importance of in-service training highlights the appropriateness of flexible, self-learning delivery systems that are modular in design, user-focused and friendly.

Many of these attributes are found in the environmental training activities undertaken by the United Nations Environment Program's Network for Environmental Training at Tertiary Level in Asia and the Pacific. The large multiplier effects achieved by training staff in tertiary institutions are consistent with the enormous and escalating demand for environmental training in the Asia-Pacific region.

Introduction

A recent issue of *Industry and Environment*, a publication of the Industry and Environment Program Activity Centre of the United Nations Environment Program (IEPAC/

UNEP), notes that the effect of industry on the environment is substantial. However, whether the impacts are beneficial or detrimental depends, to a large extent, on the attitudes, knowledge and skills of those who work in industry. For this reason, industry has become one of the most important targets for environmental education and training, with five major themes being addressed:

- environmental education for engineers and other professionals, where there is a need to shift the training emphasis from pollution control towards the concepts of cleaner production and eco-efficiency by making the environment an integral part of the overall education of all industry personnel, including engineers, architects, technologists and scientists;

- greater all-round environmental awareness as consumers, suppliers and regulators, as well as industry itself, have a role in ensuring that industry works in harmony with the environment;

- environmental education for present and future managers, as environmental considerations must be integrated into business strategies and operations;

- training programmes for environmental specialists who, despite their diversity, are all of the greatest importance to industry's overall progress towards sustainability; and

- worker education and training, recognising the importance of environmental awareness and responsibility at all levels of a company.

This paper addresses the first of these themes, particularly with respect to the role of tertiary institutions in the training of environmental engineers. The stimulus for many of the proposed initiatives is provided by Agenda 21, one of the outputs of the 1992 United Nations Conference on Environment and Development. Codner et al. (1993) suggest that the challenge is to take the proposals of Agenda 21 and develop environmental education and training programmes for engineers that are appropriate for dealing with the complex, multifaceted environmental problems of today and the future. They point out that this will require a shift in educational thinking, just as there is a shift from pollution treatment to pollution prevention. Cortese (1992) notes that:

> *"The current education of most environmental professionals is incomplete. Most are trained to deal with a subset of environmental problems, such as air pollution, water pollution, or hazardous waste, but not with environmental issues in an integrated, comprehensive fashion."*

Most technical courses stress "end-of-pipe" treatments to reduce pollution or to treat waste more efficiently (Soloviev, 1992). For example, until recently, few environmental engineering courses covered waste minimisation and the prevention of pollution through the redesign of the manufacturing process. Lewis and Hay (1991), Cortese (1992), Hay et al. (1994) and others have suggested that one reason for this limited and often inappropriate scope is the traditional, single-discipline emphasis of most university departments. This impedes the integration of environmental expertise, for it must take place across administrative boundaries. Moreover, multidisciplinary programmes are often considered to be academically less rigorous (i.e. "soft") relative to traditional single-discipline courses.

Narrow, discipline-based approaches are inconsistent with the multidisciplinary nature of environmental problems and their associated solutions. As Codner et al. (1993) and Hay et al. (1994) point out, development of strategies for the prevention and/or solution of environmental problems requires input from the natural, social and applied sciences. This needs to be reflected in the curriculum and training programmes. The challenge is to design and implement curricula that contain an appropriate mix of multidisciplinary and single-discipline knowledge and skills. Graduates will then be in a position to assess the broader issues as well as contribute to the design and management aspects in their area of specialisation. This requires an engineer to have a sound background in the physical sciences along with a broad understanding of environmental, social and political processes and issues. Communication skills and the ability to consult with, and reflect the attitudes and needs of, diverse groups are key attributes that must go along with the more conventional knowledge and skills.

According to Codner et al. (1993), the major elements of the required changes include:

- "educating the educators" about the need for environmental education of engineers and the development of appropriate curricula and programmes;

- reflecting the multidisciplinary nature of environmental problems and solutions in environmental engineering education; and

- infusing environmental issues into single-discipline engineering curricula, such as chemical engineering and civil engineering, as a complement to the training of specialists in environmental engineering.

Following Codner et al. (1993), a graduate in environmental engineering should have the background to:

- understand the processes of natural and managed environmental degradation, its causes and possible solutions;

- understand the occupational environment, its influence on human health and its relationship with the natural environment;

- understand global environmental changes and the response options;

- assess the environmental impacts and effects of the processes of modern technology, industry, land development and aquatic development and be competent in methods to avoid, remedy and mitigate adverse effects;

- incorporate environmental criteria in all stages of design, development and implementation;

- contribute to the development of effective environmental and resource management systems;

- understand the development and implementation of environmental policy; and

- comprehend the political, social and economic factors in environmental management.

Codner et al. go on to warn that environmental education and training of engineers should not be seen as a separate activity covered solely by environmental engineering. Rather, all engineering curricula should integrate environmental themes. This should not be done simply as an "add on" to existing curricula, but rather it should be integrated in a holistic manner in all courses, as a complement to the more focused environmental engineering offerings.

If the reasons for infusing environmental education and training in the engineering curriculum are so compelling, why has there not been greater progress? Hay et al. (1994) and Codner et al. (1993) suggest various reasons, including the preeminence of the traditional single disciplines, the perception of multidisciplinary programmes as "soft", lack of a sense of urgency with respect to addressing environmental problems and teaching and administrative staff being resistant to change for such reasons as innate conservatism, shortage of time, lack of suitable resource materials and an overcrowded curriculum.

This paper places tertiary-level training of environmental engineers in a new paradigm and provides a tangible example of a regional approach to addressing many of the issues identified above and elaborated in the following sections.

Background

International and Regional Initiatives

Enhancing the environmental expertise of staff in tertiary (i.e. post-secondary) institutions is a strategically important part of the overall task of capacity building through human resources development. Both the UN Conference on Environment and Development held in Rio de Janeiro, Brazil in 1992 and its formal outcome — Agenda 21 — acknowledge that job-specific training is one of the major strategies to develop human resources and, in turn, facilitate the transition to a more sustainable world. More specifically, Agenda 21 recognises the need to support university and other tertiary institutions and networks involved in education and training related to society, environment and development. Their activities can be used to enhance the abilities of people to assess and address the diverse concerns related to sustainable development, environmental quality and the quality of life.

Some of the specific training initiatives identified in Agenda 21 are:

* implement sustainable development at all points of policy- and decision-making;

* integrate environmental and development issues;

* increase skills related to environmental management in all relevant training programmes;

* develop new training programmes for existing environmentally-sound practices;

* respond to structural adjustments that impact on employment and skill requirements;

* respond to the training needs of minority, isolated and marginalised people to assist them to participate more fully in developing sustainable work practices and lifestyles;

* enhance the understanding of the relationships between sound environmental and good business practices;

* achieve universal access to technical services that support sound environmental management practices; and

- enhance the ability to access, analyse and effectively use information and knowledge on environment and development.

Many of the Agenda 21 recommendations related to environmental education and training grew out of initiatives of the International Environmental Education Programme, a joint activity of the United Nations Programme (UNEP) and the United Nations Educational, Scientific and Cultural Organisation (UNESCO). The declaration and recommendations of the Intergovernmental Conference on Environmental Education held in Tbilisi in 1977 provided fundamental principles for the enhancement of education, public awareness and training. These were updated and strengthened in the recommendations and framework for action prepared at the "World Conference on Education for All: Meeting Basic Learning Needs", which was held in Jomtien, Thailand in 1990. Together, they provide the basis for the education, public awareness and training proposals found in Agenda 21.

Environmental education and training specialists from the Asia-Pacific region anticipated such needs and responses when they met in Bangkok in 1985 (UNEP, 1986) and proposed a programme of action for environmental education and training in the region. They identified an urgent need to develop curricula for tertiary-level environmental education, placing a high priority on those specific issues that:

- would provide a better understanding of the holistic nature of environmental problems;

- were of immediate concern to most countries in the region; and

- would be gaining considerable urgency in the near future.

The specialists also proposed that the need for greater collaboration and interaction in environmental education in Asia and the Pacific be addressed by the establishment of a regional network of institutions and individuals active in environmental education and training.

It is within this context that UNEP's Network for Environmental Training at Tertiary Level in Asia and the Pacific (NETTLAP) was established, with the project's activities emphasising the need for networking activities related to the development and dissemination of curriculum guidelines, resource materials, instructional tools and training packages. UNEP's regional initiative in environmental training received further endorsement from the Regional Consultative Meeting on Environmental Training at Tertiary Level in Asia and the Pacific held in Bangkok, Thailand in 1993 (UNEP/ROAP, 1993). Further details of NETTLAP activities are contained in a later section of this paper.

Regional Context
The regional setting has a profound influence on both the focus and nature of the environmental training activities undertaken. The Asia-Pacific region covers 23 percent of the world's land area, extending from the Islamic Republic of Iran in the west to the Cook Islands in the east, and from Mongolia in the north to New Zealand in the south. It also incorporates a vast oceanic area, including the world's largest ocean, the Pacific, as well as the Indian Ocean and numerous important seas.

Over 55 percent (3.17 billion) of the world's inhabitants live in the region. Three of the five most populous countries are in the region (China with 1.19 billion, India with 880 million and Indonesia with 185 million), but there are also countries with populations of less than 20,000 people. While some 70 percent of the region's inhabitants live in rural areas, the annual population growth rate of 3.7 percent for urban areas, as opposed to 1.5 percent for rural areas, highlights the fact that the region is undergoing rapid urbanisation. Mega-cities are now a feature of Asia — of the 21 most populous cities in the world, 13 are located in the Asia-Pacific region.

The region is characterised by its diversity — environmental, economic, cultural, social and political. Such diversity gives the region its identity and much of its global significance, but it also presents an enormous challenge to those who are required to characterise the region or attempt to find commonalities for regionally-based cooperative initiatives. The difficulties are exemplified in the present study, which attempts to identify the factors governing and influencing environmental training in the region as a whole and from there to develop guidelines for future training initiatives.

The Asia-Pacific region does share at least one common characteristic — an unfortunate attribute of escalating environmental degradation. Virtually all indicators of environmental quality are revealing deteriorating conditions (ESCAP, 1992). Faced with a rapidly growing population seeking a higher standard of living and rapid economic growth (the region averaged 6.8 percent in the 1980s, over twice the world average of 3 percent), the region must move quickly to harmonise the often conflicting goals of environmental protection, resource conservation, economic development and social progress (Hay et al., 1994).

Implications for the Asia-Pacific Region

Targeted training is a key to meeting the challenges implicit in the goals of environmentally sound, sustainable and equitable development. Increased quality and relevance of the educational and training roles performed by tertiary-level educators will not only result in more skilled and knowledgeable students graduating from these institutions, but decision makers and policy formulators from both the public and private sectors will also benefit significantly from formal and informal interactions with tertiary staff. UNEP's NETTLAP is one of the regional initiatives designed to increase the capacity of the region to arrest environmental degradation while at the same time achieving economic and social progress. Its development and on-going activities have been influenced strongly by the factors described in the following section.

Environmental Training — Influences and Imperatives

There is widespread recognition within the public and private sectors and in the community at large that degradation of the environment must be arrested, that natural resources are being used at an unsustainable rate and that legitimate demands for an improved quality of life and enhanced environmental quality must be answered. However, a number of other less obtrusive but equally important factors are also driving the rapid evolution of our attitudes, and our actions, regarding the environment. A complex array of environmental and socioeconomic factors are working to influence the policies and work programmes related to environmental management and problem solving. This section will attempt to identify the dominant influences and outline some of the implications for the training of environmental engineers at the tertiary level.

Pervasive Influences

As indicated in the previous section, significant changes in the goals, attitudes, values and approaches concerning environment and development have occurred over the past few decades, and many are ongoing. The major reformations include:

- movement towards the sustainable use of resources and management of the environment, with a symbiotic relationship between environment and development;

- greater awareness of the intrinsic linkages in natural and managed systems, leading to the need for multidisciplinary and integrated approaches to both environmental and resource management and related problem solving;

- recognition that the complexity of human-environment interactions and the consequent uncertainties necessitate adoption of a precautionary approach in environmental policies, technology and management;

- acknowledgment that conventional Western approaches to economic development and social progress may not be appropriate for developing countries in the Asia-Pacific region;

- realisation that the industrial technologies and processes favoured by developed countries in the West may not be optimal for developing countries in the Asia-Pacific region;

- movement from centrally-planned to free-market economies, with consequent changes in implementation of environmental policies and plans;

- movement away from treating the environment as a "free good" towards internalising environmental costs by incorporating them in the decisions of producers and consumers, and using integrated and comprehensive approaches to environmental, economic and social accounting, where appropriate;

- increased use of economic and, particularly, market-oriented approaches in development policies and in laws and regulations related to environmental protection;

- movement away from legislative and regulatory limits on activities towards environmental management and the associated legislative principles that pay more attention to avoiding, remedying or mitigating the adverse environmental effects of those activities;

- proactive identification of the potential for environmental degradation in the planning stages of development rather than invoking environmental protection strategies and regulations that invoke retroactive application of available pollution control technologies;

- less reliance on complex technological solutions and a preference for management and remedial strategies that build on the inherent resilience and restorative capacity of natural environmental systems;

- complementing activities in pollution control and emergency response with attention to pollution prevention and hazard avoidance, using cleaner production, process efficiency and other prudent strategies;

- increased ability to monitor and assess the state of the environment and the nature and rate of environmental change;

- for many environmental systems, an enhanced ability to predict the nature and magnitude of natural and anthropogenic changes using numerical and physical models;

- an emerging global economy, which brings with it such undesirable outcomes as trans-boundary movement of hazardous wastes, trading in endangered species and transfer of technologies and products banned in some countries; and

- changing population demographics and personal career profiles, including decreased job security and increased mobility in the labour force.

Contemporary changes have occurred in the tools, technologies and methods available to environmental trainers. Among the most significant are:

- more accessible and comprehensive databases and technologies for presentation and interpretation of information;

- increased access to information processing systems and sophisticated numerical and physical models capable of realistic representations of the form and functions of complex systems;

- rapid development of personal and mass communication technologies;

- growth of education and training technologies such as interactive learning systems, distance education and simulation packages and computer-aided instruction;

- increased availability and use of self-learning packages; and

- new delivery systems for distance learning, such as voice mail and satellite communication allowing interactive video.

Another significant change has occurred in the composition of the "client base" of tertiary institutions. This has been reflected in new demands with respect to the content, delivery methods and assessment procedures used in the environmental education and training programmes offered by tertiary institutions in the region. Staff in these institutions may now find themselves interacting with and providing services to:

- students in degree, diploma and certificate programmes;

- government officials;

- research sponsors;

- representatives of industry and commerce;

- non-governmental organisations, community groups and individuals; and

- short-course participants.

In developing countries where environmental expertise is limited, staff of tertiary institutions have a particularly important role to play through the provision of policy and technical advice to governments and industry.

Imperatives for Environmental Training
In this paper, the conventional approach to preparation and dissemination of training materials, the so-called RDDA model, is rejected. This involved a linear sequence — research, design, develop and adopt.

The preferred approach for the development and dissemination of training materials involves:

- adopting a decentralised approach;
- identifying the target group and its diverse needs;
- developing local support;
- ensuring local ownership;
- encouraging local propagation of activities;
- achieving large multiplier effects;
- focusing on in-country training;
- guaranteeing an on-going commitment; and
- making the programme self-sustaining.

The considerable diversity of needs and capacities that exist in tertiary institutions in the Asia-Pacific region demands that environmental training methods be flexible, adaptable and non-prescriptive. Of similar importance are:

- use of the vernacular, wherever appropriate;
- a reliance on action-oriented and participatory methods;
- achieving a balance between passing on knowledge, exploring and affirming values and developing skills;
- incorporating traditional knowledge and practices;
- ensuring cultural and political sensitivity; and
- addressing equity issues.

Responses: Environmental Training Strategies

According to Mena (1993), the foremost response must be in-service training of the teaching staff in environmental engineering as this is an important way to promote institutional changes. These include integration of environmental topics in existing courses as well as the introduction of new courses. Such innovations can succeed only if the engineering teacher believes in the curricular changes and takes the lead. Before dealing with the pre- and in-service training of environmental educators and trainers, it is appropriate to identify responses that should be included in the curricula and delivery systems for engineering students. These will define the desirable content of staff training programmes.

Curriculum and Delivery-oriented Responses

Mena (1993) argues that further development of environmental engineering curricula should be guided by a UNESCO recommendation on engineering education:

> *"Engineering education should transform its traditional scientific-technical-economic frame of reference into one in which the social and environmental sciences play a broader multidisciplinary role."*

In this context, he calls for innovation in engineering education and training in order to:

- equip engineers with attitudes and work methods that will cope with change in technological practices;

- encourage students to develop skills in design and give them a chance to demonstrate any aptitude for invention; and

- have students investigate problems, simple and complex, as members of a team and as individuals.

He notes that since the propensity for innovation depends on the pattern or structure of the education process some innovations may have great value and thus be worth adopting in one country, but may be considered as too demanding in other countries. Likewise, innovations appropriate for some institutions may not be suitable in others. With this caveat, Mena proposed several strategies for improving the quality and relevance of education and training in environmental engineering:

- where appropriate, introduce the students to the history of technology and to the current state of industry and industrial organisation, for students must be able to appreciate fully the role of technology in the development of society;

- students should be encouraged not only to develop skills in design but also in incorporating their own inventions and innovations, as well as those of others (for example, in addition to the traditional methods of waste treatment, students must consider waste minimisation techniques as strategies for hazardous waste management);

- in problem-based teaching, students should have the opportunity to investigate both simple and complex problems as members of a team and thereby come to appreciate the value of different perspectives and multidisciplinary and interdisciplinary approaches to problem solving; and

- use of seminar courses where opportunities should be provided for a full exchange of views about up-to-date developments in environmental engineering between students and senior representatives from government and the private sector.

Mena highlights a dilemma often faced by curriculum planners when implementing these strategies — namely that further input of fresh material strains an already overcrowded curriculum. The first approach is that of infusion — to introduce new and relevant developments in technological practices in existing courses, wherever possible. Otherwise, a curriculum review may be required to identify the necessary changes and how they can be accommodated.

Training-oriented Responses

For the Asia-Pacific region, the diverse backgrounds, aspirations and support for staff from tertiary institutions undertaking environmental training places a premium on the development and application of flexible approaches and the technologies that support them. This should include:

- provision for on-demand and on-going in-service training;

- the use of flexible learning systems that are modular in construction and both user-focused and friendly;

- the use of self-learning and distance learning delivery systems, with short periods of intensive group learning;

- adoption of existing educational and training packages, wherever possible, and with adaptation to local conditions (e.g. language, case studies, regulations, cultural values) where necessary or desirable; and

- forging partnerships between tertiary educators, industry and commerce to benefit not only from a better understanding of "client" needs and of industrial processes and commercial practices, but also from a transfer of training technologies and methods, since these are often pioneered by the private sector.

Case Study — The NETTLAP Approach to Environmental Training

For a region as large and diverse as Asia and the Pacific, how is it possible to have a significant impact on the quality and relevance of environmental training in tertiary institutions, including universities, technical institutes and teacher training colleges? Fortunately, enhancing the environmental knowledge and skills of a tertiary educator or trainer has the benefit of a large multiplier effect, for one environmental educator or trainer in a tertiary institution can upgrade the environmental skills and awareness of hundreds of students. Upon graduation, many will move into positions of responsibility where they apply the acquired environmental expertise. Through informal education and training programmes, such as short courses or public lectures, this same staff member is also able to enhance the skills and awareness of key individuals in government, the private sector and the community at large. The effectiveness of this transfer process is even greater if the staff member passes on some of his/her expertise to colleagues in his/her own institution, or elsewhere.

Thus, training of tertiary staff is very cost-effective and efficient. The critical factor in this approach is identification of key tertiary educators who will incorporate the information and techniques into both their formal and informal teaching and training activities. A major frustration arises from the fact that only a small proportion of tertiary educators can participate in intensive, personalised training programmes by which the knowledge and skills are transferred. Again there is a solution that, fortunately, also has a large multiplier effect.

The key is the Resources Development Workshop (RDW), which brings together resource persons and participants who are all recognised for their expertise and experience, not only in the thematic focus of the workshop but also in the learning systems that can be used in education and training. In particular, those attending the workshop are acknowledged as being highly successful educators and trainers. The workshop enables them to share the approaches and materials that contribute to this success. Individually and jointly, these people apply their knowledge and skills to the development of a number of resources — hence, the concept of the RDW, as opposed to conventional training workshops. The resources that are developed during and as a direct result of the RDW include:

- development of the individual and combined knowledge and skills of the workshop participants;

- development of curriculum guidelines for education and training activities;

- development of instructional resource materials to support the education and training activities in tertiary institutions;

- development of instructional aids (e.g. computer-assisted learning software) to support the education and training activities in tertiary institutions; and

- development of integrated training packages.

When disseminated, the workshop outputs lead directly to institutional strengthening and human resources development — the latter initially in the tertiary institutions and ultimately, through the graduates and short courses, in government, the private sector and the community. The full involvement of experienced educators in this process ensures that the materials are targeted at the regional and even more localised needs, capacities and objectives of their peers. They also address the impediments to widespread acceptance and application.

Over the past two years, UNEP's NETTLAP has developed, implemented and evaluated these approaches, while at the same time building up a network of experts and practitioners in environmental education and training in tertiary institutions throughout the Asia-Pacific region. The network has grown rapidly. It was launched with the identification of National Focal Points (NFPs). These have responsibility for policy, major procedural decisions and financial resourcing at the national level. The strengths of the network are its institutional and individual members. These are supported at the regional level by Thematic Network Coordinators and at the national level by Specialist Focal Points, both related to the themes of NETTLAP — currently coastal zone management, environmental economics and toxic chemicals and hazardous waste management. The current numbers of participants are given in Table 1.

While the development of NETTLAP was catalysed by UNEP, the effectiveness of environmental training of staff in tertiary institutions will be reinforced if other governmental and non-governmental organisations use NETTLAP to increase access to and the use of the outputs of their programmes. If more targeted programmes are required, these can be facilitated by adding to the current three thematic networks — toxic chemicals and hazardous waste management, coastal zone management and environmental economics.

Summary and Conclusions

Population growth and economic, social and cultural changes in the Asia-Pacific region are resulting in escalating degradation of the environment, making it imperative that sustainable approaches to resource use and environmental management are imple-

Number of participating countries	38
Number of National Focal Points	37
Number of Thematic Networks	3
Number of Specialist Focal Points	24
Number of Institutional Members	165
Number of Individual Members	1725

Table 1: *Current level of participation in NETTLAP.*

mented without delay. A key ingredient in achieving this response is the availability of environmentally competent engineers.

Demand for such expertise will only be met if tertiary institutions in the region expand their training programmes for environmental engineers and ensure that the approaches used and the knowledge and skills transferred are consistent with the multidisciplinary nature of environmental problems and the appropriate response strategies. The environmental education of engineers must incorporate social, economic, political and legal perspectives as well as those of the natural sciences. Training will also enhance communication skills and the ability to consult with, and reflect the attitudes and needs of, diverse groups.

Through NETTLAP, UNEP is supporting such initiatives in tertiary institutions in the region. The large multiplier effects achieved by training staff in tertiary institutions are consistent with the enormous and escalating demand for environmental training in the Asia-Pacific region. NETTLAP encourages and supports the use of decentralised and flexible approaches to environmental training in order to ensure local ownership of the process and accommodate the diversity of the region. Similarly, training methods are adaptable in order to incorporate local traditional knowledge and practices and foster political and cultural sensitivity. The importance of in-service training also highlights the appropriateness of flexible, self-learning delivery systems that are modular in design and user-focused and friendly.

Acknowledgements

Appreciation is extended to the United Nations Environment Programme and, in particular, its Regional Office for Asia and the Pacific, for providing financial support to present this paper at the Workshop on the Fundamentals of Environmental Engineering Education held at the University of Canterbury, Christchurch, New Zealand from August 22 to 24, 1994.

The University of Auckland is thanked for granting the author leave to attend the Workshop.

References

Codner, G, D Huisingh and M S Jordensen (1993). "Environmental Education for Engineers". *Industry and Environment.* 7: 23-26.

Cortese, A D (1992). "Education for an Environmentally Sustainable Future". *Environment Science Technology.* 26(6): 1108-1114.

ESCAP (1993). *State of the Environment in Asia and the Pacific 1990.* Bangkok, Thailand: United Nations Economic and Social Council for Asia and the Pacific.

Hay, J E, Chou Loke Ming, B Sharp and N G Thom (1994). *Environmental and Related Issues in the Asia-Pacific Region: Implications for Tertiary Level Environmental Training.* Bangkok, Thailand: UNEP/ROAP Network for Environmental Training at Tertiary Level in Asia and the Pacific (NETTLAP). Publication No. 1.

Lewis, G and J E Hay (1991). "Environmental Teaching at the University of Auckland: An Integrated Approach". *Proceedings, Environmental Education Conference.* Palmerston North, September 1991.

Mena, M (1993). "Integration of Toxic and Hazardous Waste Management in the Curriculum". *Contributions to the Management of Toxic Chemicals and Hazardous Wastes in the Asia-Pacific Region and Report of the First NETTLAP Resources Development Workshop for Education and Training at Tertiary Level in Toxic Chemicals and Hazardous Waste Management.* Eds. J E Hay and N G Thom. UNEP/ROAP Network for Environmental Training at Tertiary Level in Asia and the Pacific Publication No. 5. Bangkok, Thailand: United Nations Environment Program.

Soloviev, E (1992). "A New Dimension in Environmental Education and Training", *Environmental Engineering — A Challenge for Europe.* Vienna: SEFI Working Group on Environmental Engineering. 44-50.

UNEP (1986). *Environmental Education & Training in Asia and the Pacific.* Bangkok, Thailand: United Nations Environment Program.

UNEP/ROAP (1993). *Environmental Training at Tertiary Level in Asia and the Asia-Pacific.* Report of the Regional Consultative Meeting on Environmental Training at Tertiary Level in Asia and the Pacific, United Nations Environment Programme (UNEP), Regional Office for Asia and the Pacific (ROAP), Network for Environmental Training at Tertiary Level in Asia and the Pacific (NETTLAP). NETTLAP Publication No. 8. Bangok, Thailand: United Nations Environment Program.

From Reductionist to Systems Thinking: The Engineering Imperative

John St J S Buckeridge
Department of Civil and Environmental Engineering
UNITEC Institute of Technology
Auckland, New Zealand

Abstract

Western educational philosophy in both technology and science is traditionally reductionist, whereby methodologies employed to understand the environment involve reducing a problem to its simplest (and most readily understood) level. In doing so, a holistic understanding of problems and recognition of effects of actions outside their immediate context were frequently not realised. In the latter half of the twentieth century, dwindling natural resources, coupled with a population explosion, facilitated the concurrent development of systems thinking, resource management, sustainability, biodiversity and environmental engineering. These concepts are considered in this paper, with the resultant effects they now engender in engineering education. Civil engineering, in particular, is shown to be the discipline in which the knowledge base residing within the biological sciences may synthesise with that of inanimate processes and design. However, this is achievable only through a systems approach to environmental management. The importance of systems thinking in "environmental" engineering is discussed, and although a core systems course will go some way toward producing effective practitioners for the twenty-first century, the need to adopt a systems approach throughout the degree programme is endorsed.

Introduction

Engineering involves the manipulation of resources — their usage, development and design. In this sense, engineering necessitates a modification of our environment.

A process that modifies our environment must recognise any potential effects of that modification, and this is enshrined in current New Zealand legislation such as the Resource Management Act (1991), which requires that:

> "... the use, development and protection of natural and physical resources (be carried out) in a way, or at a rate, which enables people and communities to provide for their social, economic and cultural wellbeing and for their health and safety."

Further to this, the Act specifies the duty of individuals as:

> "... to avoid, remedy, or mitigate any adverse effect on the environment arising from an activity carried on by or on behalf of that person ..."

This duty clearly infers a moral obligation on behalf of practitioners, such as engineers, in the manner in which they modify their environment (Buckeridge, 1992).

It follows then that the term "environmental engineering" is in reality a misnomer. All engineering *must* by current definition be *environmental*, with the environmental ethic being instilled at the quintessence of any resource management or resource development decision or endeavour (Buckeridge, 1994).

The concept of *environmental sustainability* and the imperative for maintaining *biological diversity* (see Ministry of External Relations and Trade, 1992) have arisen following the realisation that the earth's resources are indeed finite and that the rapidly growing human population is increasingly competing for what little remains. This view is not new — it was proposed by Malthus (1789), and more recently by Young (1992) and Hardin (1968), the latter using an analogy in his "Tragedy of the Commons" to illustrate that one individual really does make a difference.

Application of Technology
Mankind's quest to understand and modify our environment has been apparent since our first attempt at habitation. The philosophical approach adopted has varied through time, and has generally reflected the sophistication of society (see Figure 1).

During the seventeenth century, the philosopher Descartes proposed that the only way in which phenomena (= the environment) could be understood was through a reductionist approach, i.e. that only by breaking a problem down to its simplest elements could it be understood. This reductionism has subsequently pervaded our culture, in particular our education system, for in order to understand anything, it was necessary to disassemble it, either literally or figuratively.

Engineering students in particular, choose to become involved in technology because of an interest in understanding how and why things work. The very nature of this "mechanistic methodology" places limitations on lateral thinking. Engineering education, although more holistic than that of "science", traditionally incorporates a reductionist approach as a primary means of achieving knowledge transfer.

This provides a paradox: the holism required of a professional (or vocational) oriented educational programme and the reductionist mind-set of many of the teachers and students within that programme. This is presently being addressed at some tertiary institutions by introducing systems science as a core component of technology degrees.

Following the advice and guidance of Professor David Elms, UNITEC's Department of Civil and Environmental Engineering introduced a *systems* course as a compulsory component of the four-year Bachelor of Technology (Environmental) (Buckeridge, 1993). The objectives of the course are to:

• instil an appreciation of scientific methodology as a precursor to systems thinking;

• engender an appreciation of time and flux and the significance of these in systems design and systems modelling;

• provide a clear understanding of the nature of natural and modified systems; and

• enable students to perform systems analyses on problems in both science and engineering such that the interaction of components within these systems be recognised and effects limited.

The fundamental difference between resource "development" and resource "management" is the *accountability* of the practitioner. In Figure 1B, the model proposed for

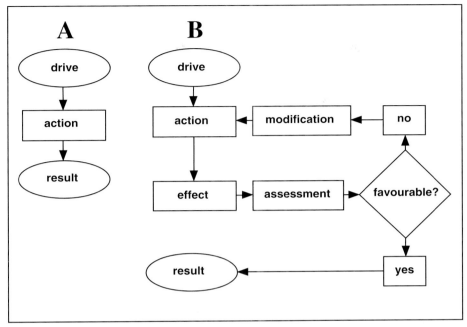

Figure 1: *Two systems analyses for mankind and the environment. **A:** A representation of an unsophisticated interaction with the environment. The system is linear (and open), lacking any feedback mechanism (or control). The implication is that "effects" are irrelevant and that the environment is capable of infinite self repair. **B:** A system demonstrating the sophisticated environmental interaction expected in modern resource usage and modification. The "drive", although likely to be the same as in A, is subjected to evaluation. Any planned action (and also the result) may thus be significantly modified in light of potential effects to the environment.*

resource usage involves a feedback loop, or control. Significantly, a representation such as this recognises that the observer (modeller or engineer) is not remote from the system proposed, but is an essential component.

Mankind's potential for environmental modification is now at its zenith. In light of this, the likelihood of significant environmental damage is very real.

The practitioner must be able to demonstrate that consideration of potentially deleterious effects has been made. This is initially performed through *scoping*, a process whereby possible environmental, social, physiological and cultural effects are assessed. The process is achieved by communicating the nature of the proposed changes to the wider community and requesting feedback (see Figure 2). A period follows during which reaction to the proposal(s) and subsequent modifications are made, with these being communicated back to the community. At the outset of any scoping, it is critical that the practitioner appreciate the system(s) in which any proposal will function. There will be a need to define the system components, establish the significance of these components (i.e. establish a hierarchy) and define the nature of the linkages between these components (Figure 2).

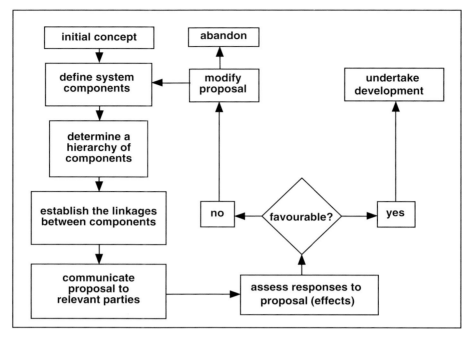

Figure 2: *Systems approach to scoping and environmental modification. Each "component" of the system, although discrete in itself, must function as part of the whole in order that the system successfully operate. "Relevant parties" include all aspects of the wider community likely to be affected by the proposal. The control mechanism permits feedback from this "community" and provides a basis from which proposed mitigation of any deleterious effects may be assessed. If the proposal is significantly modified, the original proposal may need to be completely reappraised or abandoned.*

Systems thinking has been proposed as a *metadiscipline* (Checkland, 1981). The ramifications of this definition are that systems thinking overarches other branches of science and engineering. It is unlikely that any one practitioner will have the intellectual abilities necessary to assess all aspects of any environmental management proposal. Thus the essential nature of systems thinking, and the interrelationship it establishes between disciplines, will necessitate strong communication and negotiation skills.

The most difficult aspect of any systems approach will be the *identification* and *ranking* of components of the system. In many instances, the final judgment will have a strong subjective bias and, in this case, it is hoped the project engineer (or coordinator) can demonstrate that those judgments made were based upon realistic and reasonable criteria. A formidable task.

Conclusions

The global attitude pervading at the close of this millennium is one that will reward those who adopt a responsible attitude to resource management. Systems thinking and systems modelling provide such a framework upon which our world and its rich natural diversity may be sustained. Educational programmes that adopt the philosophy embodied in systems science, particularly if it is integrated throughout the programme, will provide the intellectual environment conducive to sound future environmental management.

Acknowledgments

The author wishes to thank Dr Jack Ding, Research Fellow at UNITEC, for helpful comments, and Ian Anderson, Dean of Technology, UNITEC, who critically read this manuscript.

References

Buckeridge, J S (1992). "Morality and Resource Management: what are the issues?". *Proceedings from the New Zealand Institute of Surveyors Annual Conference*. Invercargill, 15-20 October 1992.

Buckeridge, J S (1993). "Environmental Engineering : To what degree?" *Future Trends and Challenges in Engineering Education*. Proceedings of the International Conference on Engineering Education '93, Singapore, 10-12 November.

Buckeridge, J S (1994). "Philosophy and Ethics : now an integral component in Engineering Education". *Proceedings of the Institute of Professional Engineers New Zealand Annual Conference*. Nelson, February, 1994. 1: 1-7.

Checkland, P (1981). *Systems Thinking, Systems Practice*. Chichester: John Wiley & Sons.

Hardin, G (1968). "Tragedy of the Commons". *Science*. 162: 13.

Malthus, T R (1798). *An essay on the Principle of Population*. Reprinted as "Population: the first essay". Ann Arbor: University of Michigan Press. 1959.

Ministry of External Relations and Trade (1992). *Outcomes of the United Nations Conference on Environment and Development*. Wellington: Ministry of External Relations and Trade.

Resource Management Act (1991). *An Act to restate and reform the law relating to the use of land, air, and water*. Wellington: New Zealand Government Print.

Young, M D (1992). "Sustainable investment and resource use: Equity, environmental integrity and economic efficiency". *Man and the Biosphere*. Series 9. New Jersey: Parthenon Publishing. 1-176.

The Fundamentals of Environmental Engineering Education

Marino M Mena
College of Engineering
University of the Philippines
Quezon City, Philippines

Abstract

The engineer plays an important role in development and change. However, the traditional concept of development has been a compromise between what is technically feasible and what is considered economically attractive. The increasing environmental problems associated with engineering development projects has made the engineering profession modify this traditional concept. This means that today development has to be a compromise between what is technically feasible, what is considered economically attractive and what is acceptable on environmental grounds. If engineers can be educated and trained with regard to the important environmental issues of the day, they would then be better prepared to understand the environmental consequences of their actions. This is the essence of the environmental education and training of engineers.

Introduction

Engineering is among the world's oldest professions, with hundreds of thousands of practitioners worldwide, and is a licensed profession in most parts of the world. The progress of engineering can be associated with developments in materials and construction, transportation, machines and manufacture, heat energy, electrical energy and communications. Of course, it goes without saying that discoveries in science have contributed to this progress. The development in construction, for example, has been chiefly in the materials used and the substitution of mechanical devices to reduce the amount of human labour.

Engineering progress has, therefore, been characterised by more economical costs of production. The task of engineering has always been to manipulate the materials and forces of nature for the use of man, and the engineering profession has been successful in this regard. To this end, however, the engineer has applied his technology to achieve the immediate task but, in most cases, without adequate consideration of the environmental implications. This is our concern today. The engineering profession can no longer perform its task without giving due consideration to the environmental consequences of its actions. Engineering education must, therefore, find ways to enable present and future engineers to cope with this additional responsibility in the engineering profession.

The Field of Environmental Engineering

The response of engineering educators to demands from society for a better environment is the institution of a new field in engineering, environmental engineering. But what is environmental engineering? What are its fields of practice?

The following definitions were adopted by the Third National Conference on Environmental Engineering Education held at Drexel University in August 1973:

> *"Environmental engineering is that branch of engineering which is concerned with (1) the protection of human populations from the effects of adverse environmental factors; (2) the protection of environments both local and global from the potentially deleterious effects of human activities; and (3) the improvement of environmental quality for man's health and well-being."*

Fields of practice in environmental engineering are as follows:

- Sanitary engineering is the field of environmental engineering concerned with:

  — the protection of human health from water-borne diseases and toxic materials that could be conveyed by water supply;

  — the provision of an adequate supply of water of appropriate quality for municipal and industrial use; and

  — the treatment and disposal of waste waters in such a manner so as to protect the quality of surface and ground water resources.

- Industrial hygiene engineering is the field of environmental engineering concerned with protecting people from the physical, chemical and biological hazards of their work environment.

- Air pollution control is the field of environmental engineering concerned with the collection and transformation of gaseous and aerosol wastes for the purpose of maintaining air quality in the community, protecting human health, preventing economic damage and providing an aesthetically pleasing atmosphere.

- Radiation and hazard control is the field of environmental engineering concerned with the protection of the general population from radiation and the physical, chemical and biological hazards of their total environment.

- Solid waste management is the field of environmental engineering concerned with the collection, transportation, processing, resource recovery from and ultimate disposal of solid waste.

- Environmental impact assessment is the field of environmental engineering concerned with the development and implementation of design criteria and operating procedures for structures, processes and systems that will provide for protection and improvement of environmental quality and the conservation of natural resources.

Fundamentals of Environmental Engineering Education

In the design of an environmental engineering education programme, we should consider what is expected from the environmental engineer. UNESCO defined an environmental engineer as:

> *"An environmental engineer could be considered as an engineer able to identify environmental problems and their social impact; to examine the various causes of these environmental problems; to evaluate the engi-*

neering aspects of man's interactions with the natural and man-made environments; to participate in the design of development strategies which could satisfy human needs and protect the environment; to contribute to multidisciplinary teams in relation to development planning."

What, then, are the fundamentals of environmental engineering education? The general objective is to prepare men and women to practice the profession and to make contributions to the advancement of the science of environmental engineering. To this end, the following foundation courses are needed:

- fundamentals of mathematics and natural science;
- fundamentals of human and social sciences;
- fundamentals of chemistry;
- fundamentals of economics;
- fundamentals of computer science;
- fundamentals of monitoring (sampling and analysing);
- fundamentals of systems analysis; and
- fundamentals of environmental management, which includes:
  - —corrective and preventative policies of pollution control;
  - —administration and environmental laws;
  - —environmental impact assessment and industrial siting;
  - —technologies for waste water treatment;
  - —technologies for air emission control;
  - —technologies for solid waste disposal;
  - —techniques for noise reduction;
  - —techniques for environmental modelling;
  - —non-waste technologies or techniques for waste minimisation; and
  - —the working environment.

Forms of Environmental Education and Training for Engineers

The environmental education and training of engineers must meet the needs of all engineers, regardless of whether they specialise in environmental engineering.

The first type of programme (i.e. for engineers not specialising in environmental engineering) requires that the curricula for the undergraduate degrees (e.g. BSCE, BSChE, BSMetE, BSEM, BSME, BSEE, BSGE, BSIE, etc.) must be modified so that relevant environmental issues are integrated in each curriculum. This can be achieved in two ways:

- By the institution of new courses in environmental engineering as additional requirements in each undergraduate program. For example, a course on technology and environment, the purpose of which is to expose the students to the environmental impacts of engineering projects.

- By the integration of relevant environmental issues in existing courses in the curriculum. For example, integration of environmental criteria in the design of structures, processes and systems.

The second type of programme (i.e. for engineers specialising in environmental engineering) can be in two forms:

- BS in Environmental Engineering; and

- MS in Environmental Engineering.

The BS programme has already been instituted in some universities. However, there are differences of opinion as to whether specialisation in environmental engineering should be a separate undergraduate course or whether it should be additional to conventional courses in the existing engineering disciplines. I share the opinion of many that a student should first complete a conventional course in engineering (e.g. BSCE, BSChE, BSME, etc.), including the basic environmental component, which should be common to all engineers, and then if he/she wishes to specialise in environmental engineering, he/she could pursue an MS programme in environmental engineering.

Conclusion

The engineer is responsible for the design of structure, processes and systems within constraints set by society. These constraints now include environmental constraints. For this reason, the engineer has to be exposed in the educational process to environmental issues, concerns and sensitivities. An environmentally-educated engineer can be the protector of the environment.

References

UNESCO (1979). *Environmental Education of Engineers: Current Trends and Perspectives*. Paris: UNESCO.

Third National Conference on Environmental Engineering Education. Drexel University, 1973.

Pfafflin and Ziegler, eds. (1992). *Encyclopedia of Environmental Science and Engineering*. Volume 1.

Artifactual Engineering
as a Fundamental of Environmental Engineering

Naomasa Nakajima[1] and Hiroyuki Yoshikawa[2]
[1]Center for Engineering, University of Tokyo
[2]President, University of Tokyo
Tokyo, Japan

Introduction

Our living environment is filled with the numerous artifacts human beings have created since the dawn of history. When we trace the causes of today's serious environmental problems, we arrive at the conclusion that artifacts are affecting the environment on a global scale due to expansion in their utilisation. The environment surrounding us, whether global or local, is created and continues to be formed by various processes. Some are natural, but increasingly, the environment in which we live is also formed by human activities. Therefore, in considering the fundamentals of environmental engineering, we should focus on the primary process of the creation of environment. The factor that exerts the greatest influence on the primary process of environmental formation is the process of creating artifacts, which involves their design, manufacturing and utilisation.

We have recently began studies on artifactual engineering, a new engineering science that is closely related to these processes. We regard artifactual engineering as one of the fundamentals of environmental engineering.

Artifactual Engineering

Artifactual engineering was proposed by one of the authors, Hiroyuki Yoshikawa, the current president of the University of Tokyo, as a field of scholarship that yields solutions to the difficult problems that arise from the creation of artifacts (Yoshikawa, 1993). Artifactual engineering aims to systematise the process of creating artifacts from a different viewpoint from that of conventional engineering, wherein domains of science partitioned into many fields have been studied independently; that is, from a more comprehensive point of view.

The factor common to all of today's problems, such as global environmental destruction, expansion of the scale of accidents, coexistence of overproducing regions with those suffering from hunger, trade friction and heated competition, is that they are all derived from artifacts produced in the pursuit of safety and wealth.

Conventional engineering has not yet produced any effective knowledge that can be used to solve the above problems, and neither are the future prospects bright. Consequently, environmental problems cannot solve themselves and, in this respect, conventional engineering does not offer any solutions. Artifactual engineering was, therefore, proposed under these circumstances and is motivated by the thought that conventional engineering may need to be reviewed.

The Research into Artifacts Center for Engineering (RACE) was established at the University of Tokyo in 1992. We believe that the structural problems of conventional engineering that are presently being addressed in artifactual engineering, i.e. problems pertinent to the territoriality, deductive methods of analysis and the thinking process are worth discussing as fundamentals of environmental engineering.

It is also important to discuss the design and manufacturing methods of artifacts from a comprehensive perspective, using examples.

Territoriality

First, let us observe the current status of engineering that is considered to systematise knowledge for the process of artifact creation. In 1886, there were only seven departments in the Faculty of Engineering at the University of Tokyo, but now there are 22.

It is true that such territoriality of science has greatly contributed to the development of each domain of scholarship. When a field of scholarship is divided into smaller domains, the viewpoint on the target of the science is narrowed and, as a result, the theoretical system attains conformity and simplicity. This promotes the spread of knowledge, enhances efficiency in education and the development of scholarship is accelerated.

Investigation into the relationship between knowledge systems belonging to different domains shows that conformity between relevant systems is not often taken into consideration. For example, when a toothed gear is studied, the theory of machines deals with the sliding contact movement between tooth forms, regarding them as a rigid body and disregarding the characteristics and behaviour of the material. The theory of strength of materials deals with the elastic deformation and stress of the material, and the relationship between the two is not discussed. It is recognised that independence is maintained between different domains.

Production of artifacts based on a knowledge system for which the subject of engineering is partitioned into domains will function satisfactorily without problems in an unlimited environment. However, in a finite environment, independence among domains, which arises through differently-defined viewpoints, cannot be maintained, and interaction between domains take place. We believe that this kind of isolation of domains causes a number of problems, which affect our environment on a global scale.

Scientific Method

Another central problem in conventional engineering is the methods of analysis of systematised knowledge. In conventional engineering the higher the attainment reached by a domain, the more dominant become deductive methods of analysis, which are the typical methods in science. The knowledge produced by deductive methods of analysis is effective for understanding the "artifacts that have been created". However, it is not effective for understanding the "activity of man in the creation of artifacts".

Here let us refer to *Principia Mathematica*, the well-known book by Newton, as one of the most typical methods of analysis in science. Newton established a viewpoint on the movement of objects and derived the three universal laws of uniform motion, acceleration, and action and reaction. He showed that every incident, from the terrestrial phenomenon of an apple falling from a tree to the movement of planets in the universe, can be explained using these three laws. *Principia* provides no introduction to the three laws, i.e. the process of abduction immediately introduces the reader to the three laws following the definition of items. It then leads to the propositions that can be verified by these laws. These are written in the deductive method of analysis and extend for several hundred pages.

Here, we would like to point out that the problem in the deductive method of analysis is that a system described on the basis of the deductive theory cannot give direct instructions for people's activities, such as what action to take in solving a problem. For instance, the process of frying an egg involves a number of domains of engineering, including heat transfer engineering, hydrodynamics, rheology and solid mechanics. However, the method of frying an egg cannot be obtained from the knowledge system of any one of these domains of engineering or dynamics considered independently, however deeply a person may delve.

The Thinking Process
The process of thinking that is directly relevant to determining the guidelines for solving a problem is not deductive reasoning, but the process of abductive reasoning, which was not considered by Newton at all.

The process of determining the guidelines for action does not appear to be the same as abduction in the deduction of a law. Nevertheless, it is considered to involve the same logic. For instance, an architect's viewpoints are determined by the requests and other conditions of the client, and these viewpoints determine the boundaries of the design activity. Within this domain, a structure having particular specifications is proposed as a manifestation that satisfies all the requirements.

Just as Newton established his point of view on the movement of objects, and the architect on the basis of the requests and conditions given by a client in the above example, so in abduction the first important step is to determine the point of view. However, as discussed above, in a finite environment, determination of the viewpoint tends to lead to problems that defy solution.

Fundamentals of Environmental Engineering
One of the fundamentals of environmental engineering is the ability to discuss the usefulness and limitation of conventional engineering from the viewpoints of the territoriality, deductive method of analysis and the thinking process, considering the primary processes in the creation of environment.

In addition, as examples in design and manufacturing methods for artifacts that comprehensively incorporate various viewpoints, introduction of the following two research topics to the field of education will be of great significance:

- The inverse factory, which can recycle industrial products and play the role of a "vein" that uses artifacts as input resources, as opposed to conventional factories, which engage in "arterial activities".

- The leading design system, which can support socially-driven innovation by effectively accumulating technological seeds of knowledge (Nakajima, 1993).

References

Hiroyuki Yoshikawa (1993). "Proposal for Artifactual Engineering: Aims to Make Science and Technology Self-conclusive". *Proceedings of First International Symposium on Research into Artifacts*. Tokyo, October 1993. Separate volume.

Naomasa Nakajima (1993). "Micromachines as Intelligent Artifacts". *Proceedings of First International Symposium on Research into Artifacts*. Tokyo, October, 1993. 48-51.

Regional Papers

Brunei Darussalam

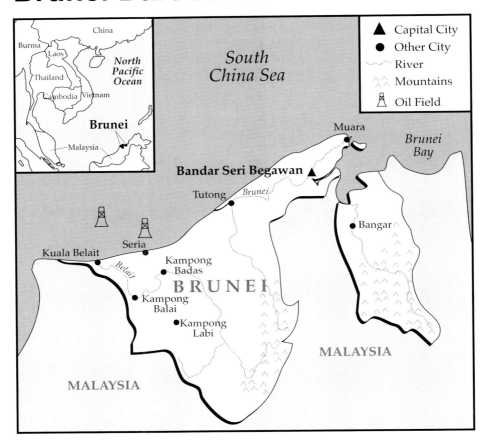

Brunei lies on the northern coast of the island of Borneo in the South China Sea. Brunei's 5765 square kilometres is occupied by 260,000 people, 70 percent of which live in the urban areas.

Brunei's economy is heavily based on the petroleum and natural gas found off the coast. Other industries include farming, forestry and manufacturing.

Most of Brunei is covered in tropical forests and rainfall averages about 250 cm a year along the coast and 320 cm inland. The Brunei River runs through the capital city of Bandar Seri Begawan, and many of the city's inhabitants live in houses built on stilts above the river.

In Brunei, education is free up to the tertiary level. Primary and secondary education is provided in Malay, Chinese and English. Most children attend primary school and many go on to secondary and tertiary education. Tertiary education includes teachers colleges, technical schools, vocational schools and university. The country's first university, Universiti Brunei Darussalam, opened in 1985.

Foundations of Environmental Engineering Education in Negara Brunei Darussalam

Mirhassan Abu Bakar and Terence Mansfield
Institut Teknologi Brunei
Bandar Seri Begawan, Brunei Darussalam

Introduction

Awareness of the need for a clean environment is becoming a global issue, and in Brunei Darussalam it is a common domestic topic. Fortunately, our environment is not as bad as in some countries, and our early understanding of the harmful effects of pollution is a bonus for our future clean environment. Fortunately, Brunein parents are alert and introduce the subject to their children at an early age, which makes them more caring towards the environment.

Implicit in the fifth and sixth five-year National Development Plans (ending in 1995) is friendliness towards the environment. This has led the Ministry of Education to pursue a future effective training system that initially responds to present and future growth sectors of industry. From the outset, Universiti Brunei Darussalam, together with a department from another ministry, has taken the leading role in educating public and private sectors through conferences, seminars, workshops and courses.

Pollution

The threshold level of pollution varies with the types of environment and pollutants. Brunei is surrounded by ASEAN countries where the degree of industrialisation is mostly in its infancy. In addition, our forests are mostly virgin and undisturbed. These factors result in a minimal level of pollution in Brunei in almost every sector.

Because of the dispersion of land-based urbanisation, exhaust emissions from motor vehicles are not a perceptible annoyance. The recent introduction of lead-free petrol should ensure that exhaust emissions have a less harmful effect on the atmosphere as the number of vehicles increases over time.

Brunei is fortunate to have a plentiful supply of potable water, which is derived from sources that are not exposed to groundwater contamination. Industrial chemical waste is not a consideration at this time, as industrial growth has only recently begun to develop in Brunei. Oil extraction has its dangers, but normal precautions are taken, such as the provision of holding lagoons to contain spillage.

Tropical rainforest covers 70 percent of the land area and, for the most part, remains undisturbed, as logging is only undertaken to satisfy domestic needs. Clear felling of trees to create space for housing developments around the urban areas does, however, cause some problems, such as erosion, siltation and visual impact. With the accelerating rate of building construction in the country, it is important to preserve areas for the enjoyment of future generations in aesthetically valuable zones, such as river banks. Iron oxides in concrete aggregates have been the source of some urban visual pollution, but the problem has been addressed by development of alternative sources of river gravel. Unsightly rust stains on buildings are also caused by use of beach sand in the concrete, but thorough washing to remove the salt overcomes this problem.

Sewage pollution is being alleviated by a programme of treatment plant construction for land-based urbanisation. On the Brunei River, a population of 30,000 inhabit a water village, which consists mainly of timber houses built on stilts. Fortunately, this water village is on a stretch of the river that benefits from tidal flushing, which reduces the impact of the current practice of discharging raw sewage into the river. However, alternative methods of disposal are being investigated.

Sanitary landfills cater for the disposal of household waste, but garbage collection is not comprehensive and the water village causes problems in this respect as the traditional method of waste disposal is to dump it directly into the river. The modern proliferation of plastic wrappings and containers makes this practice increasingly unacceptable due to the impact on marine life and the pollution of beaches. Attempts have been made to relocate the water villagers to government-provided land-based housing. Understandably, this solution has been not entirely successful as it requires a major change of lifestyle and the disruption of tightly cohesive communities.

In some respects, the water village may be regarded as an energy efficient form of housing. Location of dwellings on stilts in an area that benefits from the cooling effects of sea breezes and from thermal regulation by proximity to a large body of water obviates the need for artificial airconditioning systems. This reduces the requirement for power generation with its inherent pollution. The water village is a self-contained community with its own shops, schools and mosques in a compact area. This has the beneficial effect of reducing the need for travel by car.

Accountability
Brunei's environmental problems are not of such a scale as to require substantial new legislation, nor is it necessary to introduce punitive taxation to discourage industrial pollution. Accountability for the prevention of pollution should primarily lie with the population at large, with construction companies and with government departments. Public awareness of the issues and development of remedial or preventative measures may be more effective than additional legislation.

Remedial Action
Erosion, with its resultant siltation and visual impact, may be remedied by the reintroduction of vegetation and provision of terracing or diversionary drainage on steep slopes. Existing pollution of beaches may be remedied by a cleanup campaign requiring the involvement of the public and could be part of a public awareness-raising programme. Such a programme might be carried out in conjunction with the armed forces. In the long term, of course, the only effective remedy is prevention.

Prevention
It is perhaps a paradox of conservation that exploitation of an asset may be the only way to ensure its preservation. For example, the unique qualities of the water village and the natural beauty of the region could support the development of a viable tourist

industry, which would lead to a vested interest in environmental protection. Income would also be generated, which could enable conservation projects to take place. Investment in agriculture could serve to re-establish the traditional custodians of the land, and the development of commercial fish-farming is an additional possibility.

Increasing public awareness of the fragility of the habitat may be the single most effective way to implement environmental protection. The water village could be regarded as an asset, rather than a liability, and it is currently being extended in the traditional style using modern, less flammable building materials. Provision of satisfactory sewerage and convenient garbage collection facilities should ensure an improvement in its impact on the surrounding area. However, a reduction in littering is only possible if the villagers are conscious of the need to alter their patterns of behaviour, and this is also true for the remainder of the community.

A litter reduction campaign is a possible first step towards development of a respect for the environment. People should be encouraged to develop an appreciation of the beauty of nature and concern for the fauna that may be damaged by thoughtless disposal of garbage. The young people of today are more deeply concerned about the fragility of the environment than any previous generation. It is important that this is supplemented with sufficient knowledge so that their desire to protect their world may be realised. Parents are concerned about their children's future and may well be influenced by them.

At the primary level of education, consciousness of our dependency on natural resources should be raised by considering the necessities of life. Clean water, food and clothing are easily taken for granted, and children should be made aware of the sources of these essentials. People are a part of nature and are also dependent on it. A respect for animals and nature should be nurtured by visits to zoos, farms and areas of natural beauty.

Curriculum

In the past three decades, studies of the environment have changed some facets of the engineering curriculum. Interdisciplinary knowledge is a must for present-day engineers to enable them to have a broader outlook. Institut Teknologi Brunei (ITB) provides for the education of engineers in Brunei. It is necessary that a curriculum system at ITB is designed in a way that emphasises blending environmental studies with individual subjects in civil, mechanical and electrical engineering. To be more effective in the long run, a flow-through system should be introduced for those technical and vocational establishments that cater for a similar range of theoretical and skills training.

At the secondary level of education, it is possible that environmental studies may tend to be overlooked in the preparation of school curricula. Because the environment is now a common topic on television and in the media generally, we tend to assume that this interest is reflected in the schoolroom. This may be the case at an informal level, but it is important to include environmental studies as an integral part of school courses.

The pressures for secondary students to achieve academic success make formal incorporation of environmental study essential so that it is not neglected. It need not necessarily be a separate subject, but could be formally included in such subjects as geography, science and even the social sciences. If students in science studied the chain of events that result from burning as a method of plastics disposal, they would learn part of the science curriculum and also have the knowledge to discourage the practice. By studying science in a real situation, their learning would become relevant and, hence, more effective.

Study of the environmental impact arising from a local industry or construction project would involve students in real-life situations and encourage them to form educated opinions. Interdisciplinary cooperation and involvement of non-educational experts in the preparation of projects would be a valuable way of developing a holistic attitude to environmental issues. Environmental experts from the community should be consulted in the preparation and implementation of resource material.

Institutions that provide training for teachers are in an important position to influence both the attitudes and abilities of future teachers. Inclusion of environmental studies as a significant part of teacher training courses would be a very effective means of enhancing environmental education. Teacher training establishments could make teachers aware of the range of resource material available.

The environment is of concern to everyone and its protection should be the responsibility of all sectors of the community. At the tertiary level of education, interest in environmental issues has increased dramatically over the last three decades. However, this has traditionally been restricted to disciplines such as civil engineering, which has always involved a consideration of environmental interactions.

People who are privileged to study at the tertiary level are likely to be influential members of the community. For this reason, exposure to concepts of conservation should be included in all courses at this level. Development of a concise environmental package for inclusion in nontechnical courses would be a possible tactic to implement. A more comprehensive package could be developed for the technical and scientific subjects. Environmental studies should certainly be included in the study of economics, as provision of environmental safeguards and the additional costs incurred must be assessed and evaluated.

Conclusion

It is evident that the provision of adequate sewerage, garbage disposal facilities and slope protection measures is the responsibility of public utilities and the civil engineering profession, but the implementation of an effective campaign can only be carried out by the community. In industry and construction, measures necessary to safeguard the environment are likely to involve extra cost. Environmental experts can only advise — the decisions are made by the community. Hence, it is necessary for the general community to have sufficient appreciation of the issues in order to be able to make valid judgements.

The community can contribute directly to the quality of our environment by their everyday actions. Thoughtful disposal of garbage and other waste material should be encouraged as a first step towards environmental awareness.

Although environmental awareness can be raised by other means, educators have a special responsibility in this area so that future generations may enjoy an acceptable quality of life. Environmental studies should be incorporated in the curricula at all levels of education.

Bibliography

Institution of Civil Engineers (1990). *Pollution and Containment*. London: Thomas Telford.

UNEP (1986). *Environmental Education and Training in Asia and the Pacific*. Bangkok, Thailand: United Nations Environment Program.

China

China is the world's most populous nation and is the third largest in area. The total population is around 1.2 billion, about a fifth of the world's total.

China has several of the world's largest cities, including the capital city of Beijing (7 million people) and Shanghai (7.8 million people). China has 40 cities with populations greater than one million. However, most Chinese (80 percent) live in rural villages.

Agriculture is the main industry in China, and the population is concentrated in the eastern third of China, where the majority of the land suitable for farming is located. Crops include rice, sweet potatoes, tea and wheat. Manufacturing is also an important industry, and Shanghai is one of the world's leading manufacturing centre's. Fishing is another important industry, much of which is freshwater fishing.

The land is highly varied and includes deserts in the northeast, the Tibetan plateau in the southwest and the basin of the Chang Jiang river, Asia's longest river. Climate varies according. The desert regions receive as little as 10 cm of rain a year, while other regions receive as much as 200 cm.

In China, primary and junior middle school is compulsory. Some children go on to senior middle school and others attend vocational middle schools. Most, however, enter the workforce as labourers and farmers. Students who want to attend a tertiary institution must pass a national exam. China has several prominent universities and a television university programme. All higher education is free.

Environmental Education in China

Jiang Zhanpeng
Department of Environmental Engineering
Tsinghua University
Beijing, China

Abstract

This paper outlines the education system for environmental science and engineering in China. Since the United Nations Conference on Environment and Development at Stockholm in 1972, the Chinese government has paid considerable attention to environmental protection. More professionals working in this field are needed and a variety of courses on the environment are offered by some universities and colleges. There are now more than 60 universities and colleges that have set up the educational speciality of environmental science and engineering in China, most of which place special stress on engineering. About 11,000 undergraduate and 400 graduate students are studying in these universities and colleges for their BS, MS and PhD degrees, which were not awarded in China until 1981. Some larger universities also offer continuing education programmes to give short courses for staff and engineers engaged in the field of environmental protection.

Environmental engineering education at Tsinghua University, the largest university in China, is described in detail. In 1977, the first specialised courses in environmental engineering were established there. The speciality became a department in 1984 and now comprises six divisions: water quality and water pollution control; air pollution control; solid waste management and disposal and nuclear industry environmental engineering; environmental planning and management; environmental chemistry and monitoring; and water supply and wastewater engineering.

The department also offers continuing education programmes on environmental engineering for engineers and administrators from factories and design institutes.

Introduction

The world's environmental and ecological situation is changing for the worse. All countries are paying close attention to the situation and protecting the environment has become a common human concern.

Since 1972, when the United Nations Conference on Environment and Development at Stockholm was held, the Chinese government has paid great attention to environmental protection. A clause has been written into the Chinese constitution that effectively protects the environment and continuously improves environmental quality. The government has declared that environmental protection is a fundamental component of national policy.

Protecting the environment requires many more qualified personnel working in the field and the Chinese environmental education system is, therefore, developing rapidly.

The Chinese Education System

The Chinese education system is composed of two parts: common education and adult education.

Common education consists of primary school, secondary school and higher education. In cities and towns, some children attend kindergarten, and most children enter primary school at six years of age. Education for nine years has been compulsory since 1986 and every child must complete his/her study in primary school and junior middle school. After that, some students enter senior middle school and others enter vocational middle school. However, most students enter the workforce as labourers and farmers.

A student who wants to receive a higher education must first pass the national examination, which is held July 7-9 every year. Although many students sit the examination, only about 30% of them can be enrolled on the basis of their examination grades. Before 1981, no degree was awarded to graduates, but an educational degree is now awarded. Higher education is divided into several levels:

- simplified undergraduate (two to three years, no degree);

- regular undergraduate (Bachelor of Science, Engineering or Arts degree, four to five years);

- postgraduate, including masters (MS, ME or MA degree, two and a half to three years beyond BS, for some outstanding students two years);

- doctoral programme (PhD, ScD or MD degree, three to four years beyond MS); and

- postdoctoral programme (two years).

Chinese universities are organised in three levels — university (college), department and speciality. No tuition fee is collected from students and the universities give scholarships to about one-third of undergraduates and to all graduate students. This is starting to change and some students are now required to pay part of their tuition. Most universities and colleges provide dormitories on campus for students free of charge.

Adult education is an important part of professional training. Programmes available for adult education in China are varied and include:

- spare time education;

- continuing education;

- evening college;

- television college;

- radio college; and

- individual study to sit the national examination.

Environmental Education in China

Environmental education in China has developed into an overall education system. The system is composed of elementary, professional, in-service and social environmental education.

Elementary environmental education gives children an initial knowledge of environmental protection and usually takes the form of playing games and drawing pictures. Special lessons or courses are also offered to middle school students.

Professional environmental education started in China in the mid-1970s, and a wide range of environmental specialities were set up in a number of universities and colleges. These specialities include environmental sciences, engineering, medicine and pedagogy, in the following areas:

- environmental chemistry;
- environmental geography;
- environmental ecology;
- environmental biology;
- environmental medicine;
- environmental engineering;
- environmental monitoring;
- environmental planning and management;
- environmental protection on agriculture; and
- environmental law.

The levels of environmental education are as follows:

- 8 doctorate conferring points (4 specialities);
- 35 master points (10 specialities); and
- 91 bachelor points (16 specialities).

The total number of enrolled students is about 11,000.

Professional environmental education is, for the most part, concerned with training personnel in advanced areas.

There are three types of in-service environmental education — on-the-job training, a diploma for adults and continuing education. The first environmental protection training school for the in-service training of adults, China Environmental Management Cadre College, was founded in 1981 and a number of trainees, including high rank cadres, have received training here. Some universities offer a continuing education programme for staff and engineers engaged in the field of environmental protection. The programmes are diverse and include:

- environmental monitoring;
- water pollution control;
- atmospheric pollution control;
- solid waste disposal;
- environmental planning;

- environmental management;

- evaluation of environmental impacts; and

- environmental law.

More than 400,000 personnel have undergone such training in the past ten years. With their raised vocational level and professional ability, they have played a vital role in environmental protection.

The purpose of social environmental education is to heighten all people's awareness of environmental protection. It is necessary to teach the importance of environmental protection to government officers, factory directors and managers. Most of this is done by publicity on TV, radio and in newspapers to publicise environment protection.

Department of Environmental Engineering, Tsinghua University

As an example, environmental engineering education at Tsinghua University, the largest university in China, is discussed in detail below.

Tsinghua University is a comprehensive university and has a special stress on engineering. It was founded in 1911, and is situated in a northwestern suburb of Beijing. The University currently has a campus area of more than 3 km^2 (750 acres) and over 960,000 m^2 of floor space. It comprises 28 departments (including Architectonics, Civil Engineering, Environmental Engineering, Hydraulic Engineering, Precision Instruments and Mechanical Engineering, Chemical Engineering, Electronic Engineering, Computer Science and Engineering, Biological Sciences and Technology, Applied Mathematics, Physics, Chemistry, Chinese Literature, Foreign Linguistics), and 27 research institutes, with more than 3800 faculty members and research staff (including more than 1500 professors and associate professors, and 1000 lecturers), and over 14,000 students (including more than 2900 postgraduate students).

The Department of Environmental Engineering was established in 1984. The Sanitary Engineering Section, the department's predecessor, was founded in 1928 as a part of the Department of Civil Engineering. In 1952, this section was expanded into a speciality — Water Supply and Wastewater Engineering. In order to meet requirements for protecting the environment, the first environmental engineering speciality in China was established here in 1977. This speciality became an independent department in 1984.

The department consists of six divisions, namely:

- water quality and water pollution control;

- air pollution control;

- solid waste management and nuclear industry environmental engineering;

- environmental planning and management;

- environmental chemistry and monitoring; and

- water supply and wastewater engineering.

There are more than 100 faculty and staff members in the department, including 14 professors, 20 associate professors, and 40 lecturers, research engineers and assistants.

The department offers courses in environmental engineering for undergraduates and admits 60 freshman students each year. Undergraduate courses at Tsinghua University are five years in length, while for most universities in China it is four years. In addition, the department also admits 30 outstanding students from other departments to study environmental engineering and to receive their second Bachelor degree (taken concurrently within the five-year period). For MS students, the department offers three speciality areas — environmental engineering, municipal engineering and radioactive waste treatment. These specialities admit 20 to 25 MS students each year. For PhD students, the department offers two speciality areas, environmental engineering and radioactive waste treatment, and admits 10 new students each year. The department also has a postdoctoral programme, which admits between two and five postdoctoral researchers each year.

The academic year in the university is divided into three terms: the fall semester (18 weeks), the spring semester (18 weeks) and the summer session (six weeks). For undergraduate students, the five-year curriculum is divided up as follows: the first three years are mainly for basic scientific courses, the next one and a half years are for specialised and technical courses, and the final half year is set aside for graduate projects (thesis or design). However, this system is soon to be replaced by a credit system, with at least 240 credits being required for a Bachelor degree.

The specialised core courses in the department are:

- environmental science;

- introduction to civil engineering;

- environmental engineering monitoring;

- microbiology for environmental engineering;

- environmental hydraulics;

- water quality control engineering;

- air pollution control engineering;

- environmental systems analysis;

- environmental impact assessment;

- engineering economics and resource utilisation;

- environmental planning and management;

- process chemistry for water and wastewater treatment;

- aerosol mechanics; and

- solid waste management and disposal.

The department also offers continuing education programmes for staff and engineers working in the field of environmental protection through the School of Continuing Education on campus at Tsinghua University. In recent years, varied programmes such as environmental planning, environmental information management, wastewater treatment, water pollution control, air pollution control, acid precipitation control, solid waste management and submarine disposal for municipal wastewater, were carried out.

The department has a very active research programme. The Research Institute for Environmental Engineering was established in 1981, jointly sponsored by the State Environmental Protection Bureau and Tsinghua University.

During the past ten years, the department has completed 46 important research projects, of which five were awarded State Science and Technology Progress Prizes, the highest prizes in China. The department is now undertaking a number of important projects for China's eighth five-year plan (1990-1995). The main ongoing research projects are:

- industrial wastewater treatment of poorly biodegrading wastes such as those from dye, coke, pesticide and paper-making factories;

- recycling and reuse of municipal wastewater for industries;

- groundwater pollution control in a petroleum chemical industrial zone;

- water treatment of micro-contaminated surface resources;

- feasibility and technology of discharging municipal wastewater to sea (marine disposal);

- an integrated control strategy of acid rain in the southern part of China;

- atmospheric diffusion and the comprehensive control of air pollution in the developing coastal cities;

- treatment and disposal technology for municipal refuse and hazardous solid wastes, such as liner material for landfill sites and landfill leachate treatment;

- extraction of useful metals from electroplating process wastewater sludge;

- environmental information management systems and data bank; and

- regional environmental planning and systems analysis.

In recent years, the department has taken an active part in international academic exchanges, striving to strengthen its links and friendships with the academic circles of various countries. It sends teachers and graduate students to work and study in foreign countries, to attend international technical conferences or on investigation tours. The department also invites foreign professors and scientists to visit and to undertake research work. It has established cooperative relations with universities in the US, Canada, the Netherlands, Spain, Hong Kong, Macao, France and Japan, and with companies including Lyonnaise des Eaux-Dumez Company (France), Hitachi Chemical Company (Japan), Y S Lin Associates, Inc. (USA) and James M Montgomery Consulting Engineers Inc. (USA).

Indonesia

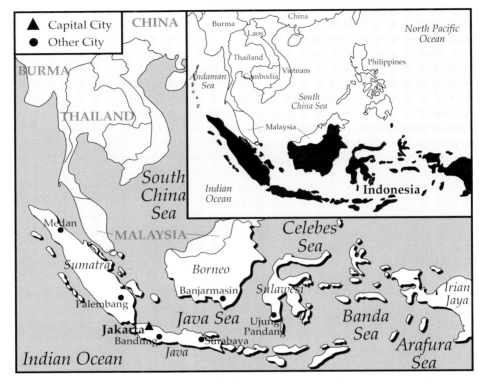

Indonesia consists of more than 13,000 islands and extends for more than 5000 kilometres along the equator. More than half of these islands are uninhabited.

Indonesia's total area is 1.9 million km² and includes the islands of Java, Sumatra, Sulawesi, about half of the island of New Guinea and three-quarters of the island of Borneo. .

Sixty percent of Indonesia's population of 197 million live on the island of Java. The country's largest cities, including the capital city of Jakarta, are also on Java. Most Indonesians live in rural villages.

Agriculture is the main industry and manufacturing is limited, but is increasing. Rice is the main product and Indonesia is one of the world's leading rice producers. Other crops include coconuts, maize, coffee, rubber and tea.

Many of Indonesia's islands are mountainous and there are about 60 active volcanoes, which means that the land is very fertile. Indonesia is rich in natural resources, and two-thirds of the country is covered in forests, including valuable hardwoods.

Three-quarters of Indonesians read and write, and children are required to attend school for a minimum of six years. Only about a third of children go on to secondary school. Some go on to tertiary education, and Indonesia has about 50 public and private universities.

Environmental Engineering Education in Indonesia

A H Djajadiningrat
Institution of Engineers Indonesia
Bandung, Indonesia

Abstract

At the Institute of Technology Bandung (ITB), Faculty of Civil Engineering and Planning, the first course in environmental engineering education was established in 1962. It was initially undertaken in the Department of Sanitary Engineering. In 1984, to meet the imperative need of conserving the environment from the pressures of rapid national development, the department widened the scope of the curriculum and research activities and changed its name to the Department of Environmental Engineering.

The major emphases in environmental engineering education are on air, water and soil environments, including systems analysis of problems associated with the environment. Nowadays, environmental engineering education has developed in other Indonesian universities (both state and private).

Introduction

The nature of engineering has changed significantly in the past two decades. Today, more than ever, engineering is interdisciplinary. It is important for all engineers to have some knowledge of all disciplines, including the relatively young branch of environmental engineering.

This paper outlines undergraduate and graduate environmental engineering courses available at the Department of Environmental Engineering (DEE), Faculty of Civil Engineering and Planning, at the Bandung Institute of Technology (ITB).

ITB has been concerned with environmental education since 1962, dealing with water quality management, environmental sanitation and public health, all of which were undertaken in the then-Department of Sanitary Engineering as a Sarjana programme (undergraduate programme). The curriculum has been changed several times since 1962 due to the increasing needs of professionals in the field of environmental engineering.

During the past two decades, the explosion in population and the expansion of human activities have caused environmental problems in Indonesia. The generation of waste continues to increase due to redevelopment in urban areas and the expansion of industrial production, particularly as high technology industries are developed. That is why, in 1984, the Department of Sanitation Engineering widened the scope of its curricula and research activities and changed its name to the Department of Environmental Engineering (DEE).

The Department of Environmental Engineering

The DEE is part of the Faculty of Civil Engineering and Planning. Located on the ITB campus in Bandung, the department conducts undergraduate and graduate study programmes. In 1993, 392 undergraduate and 34 postgraduate students were enrolled. Among the graduate students, four are studying for doctorate degrees.

The objective of the course in environmental engineering is to educate and train students to become professional engineers who know how to combine the theoretical concepts of basic subjects with engineering practice and who can integrate these into the management and solution of environmental problems. In the first and second years, basic science subjects are taught in lectures and laboratory courses in order to promote a scientific approach to environmental engineering. The subjects include:

- calculus;

- physics;

- chemistry;

- introduction to environmental engineering;

- concepts technology;

- English language;

- fluid mechanics;

- environmental chemistry;

- engineering drawing;

- engineering mathematics;

- structural engineering;

- soil mechanics;

- engineering mechanics;

- environmental microbiology; and

- epidemiology.

The third and fourth years are devoted to the application of theory through lectures, laboratory work and special assignments and practical design exercises in the following subjects:

- water and waste water treatment;

- water distribution;

- urban drainage and sewage collection;

- mechanical equipment;

- sludge management;

- unit process;

- hazards management;

- environmental quality management;

- solid waste management;

- air pollution; and

- environmental impact assessment.

In the fourth year, six-credit elective subjects are offered for further specialisation in such areas as air pollution control, environmental quality management, environmental health etc. Final year students carry out a short project.

Since 1983, the DEE has offered graduate education by conducting a postgraduate study programme, from which 35 masters degrees (magister) have been awarded. In 1992, there were 18 graduate students enrolled, two of whom were pursuing doctorate degrees.

The postgraduate programme in the DEE can be divided into two fields of study:

- environmental management and technology; and

- advanced environmental control engineering.

Graduate students take a 48-credit academic load, including six credits for their project, which is based mostly on research activities.

To support the teaching, research and community services programmes, the department operates six laboratories in:

- water quality;

- air quality;

- environmental microbiology;

- solid waste;

- hydraulics and hydrology; and

- industrial hygiene and health.

Collaboration and Links with Other Agencies

The DEE has collaborated with other agencies, both national and international, since the 1970s.

In the DEE's early years, there was joint cooperation with the University of California (Berkeley) for graduate study through United States aid programmes, which also linked the DEE with the University of Oklahoma. These programmes have resulted in three PhD and five Masters degrees being awarded.

The World Health Organisation (WHO) has also cooperated with the DEE through a technical assistance project to improve facilities and allow for staff training, including financing overseas graduate programmes for staff.

Collaborative links have been established since the 1970s between the DEE, the Technical High School of Delft and the Institute of Hydraulic and Environmental Engineering of TH-Delft. Through this, a number of overseas graduate training programmes have been conducted. Links have also been established with the International Training Network-ITB Centre, an international project financed by the UNDP-World Bank to promote low-cost water and sanitation programmes throughout developing countries. This is being done under the framework of the water decade 1980-1990, which has been further extended to "Safe Water 2000".

The ITN-ITB centre has successfully provided training for both educators and practitioners throughout Indonesia and also disseminates information on low-cost water, waste water and sanitation projects. The beneficiaries include the staffs of the Ministry of Public Works and Ministry of Health, as well as regional governments. In addition, there are links with agencies such as PERPAMSI (Indonesia Water Works Association), Pertanina (the National Oil and Gas Company) and private companies, both national and overseas. The DEE also has links with the IUC (Inter-University Centre) and the Centre for Research on Environment (Pusat Penelitian Lingkungan Hidup/PPLH ITB) to conduct research and training programmes.

As well as increasing its national and international links, the DEE has a close cooperative relationship with several government departments, such as the Department of Public Works, the Department of Health, the State Ministry for Environment, the National Agency of Environmental Impact Control and local governments.

Training programmes are periodically conducted on water quality management, waste minimisation, 3-R (reuse, recycle and recovery), clean technology, environmental audits, waste treatment technology, industrial waste water treatment, environmental impact assessment, solid waste management and other areas of interest.

References

Anon (1992). *30 years Department of Environmental Engineering Faculty of Civil Engineering and Planning ITB.*

Anon (1993). *Prospectus — ITB.*

Anon (1994). *Cantre Grant University Research Graduate Education.*

Japan

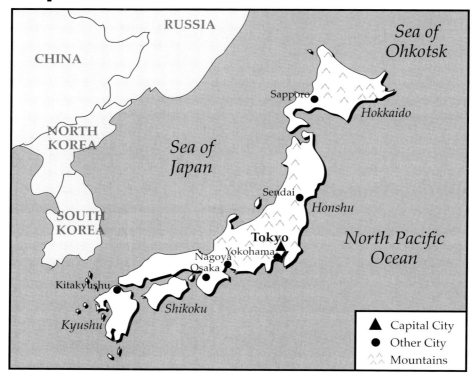

The island nation of Japan is Asia's most prosperous and industrialised country. It consists of more than 3000 islands that lie 150 to 800 km off eastern coast of Asia. The total land area is 370,000 km². More than 124 million people live in Japan and about 80 percent of these people live in towns and cities.

Much of Japan is mountainous and forests cover 70 percent of the land. Japan is not well-endowed with natural resources and the country has small quantities of most types of minerals, but not enough to be of any great value.

Farming and fishing are important industries in Japan, but the main industry is manufacturing. Japan is a world leader in the production of electronic equipment and is the second largest manufacturer of automobiles.

Education standards are high in Japan. School is compulsory for children between 6 and 14 years of age and most children complete high school. There are three types of higher learning institutions in Japan — university, junior college and technical college. There are about 60 national universities and numerous private universities.

Environmental Engineering Education in Major Japanese National Universities

N Tambo
Dean of Faculty of Engineering
Hokkaido University

Abstract

This paper summarises information on Japanese environmental engineering departments in major national universities. Of the major former Imperial Universities, the Universities of Hokkaido, Kyoto and Osaka have full-size environmental engineering departments. Tokyo University has a half-size department. Among these, the Faculty of Engineering at Hokkaido University has the largest and oldest undergraduate and graduate programmes, which were established in 1957. Kyoto and Osaka have smaller departments and graduate divisions.

The Environmental Engineering Department of Hokkaido University has 16 full professors and associate professors and 20 instructors, with 180 students taking undergraduate studies and about 100 taking graduate programmes for both MS and PhD. The department is changing the configuration for future environmental studies from classic sanitary engineering, amalgamating this with the hydrological and planning study groups of the Civil Engineering Department, urban planning and design groups of the Architecture Department and the resource management group of the Mining Department, to establish two new graduate programmes, Urban Environmental Engineering and Environmental Engineering and Environmental Resource Engineering. In addition, the Graduate School of Environmental Earth Science was established in 1993 for studying global issues, and has about 40 professors and associate professors independent from the engineering college. Details of those programmes will be presented, with other universities' organisation and curricula.

Introduction (historical sketch)

There are 98 national universities, 46 public universities and 390 private universities in Japan. Among these, 98 national universities, 27 public universities and 237 private universities have graduate schools. The number of engineering schools in national universities is 45, in public universities six, and in private universities 65.

In the field of engineering, national universities have traditionally played a major role in both research and graduate education. In the national universities, there are seven major engineering schools, in the Universities of Tokyo, Kyoto, Hokkaido, Tohoku, Nagoya, Osaka and Kyushu, all of which were imperial universities before World War II, and these, together with the Tokyo Institute of Technology, have been evaluated as the leading eight institutions. In private universities, there are several well-organised engineering schools. Until very recently, higher-level environmental education and research programmes had been carried out only in the major national universities.

The University of Hokkaido established the Department of Sanitary Engineering in 1957 as the first full-size department with both undergraduate and graduate programmes for MS and PhD degrees. The University of Kyoto followed in 1958. The University of

Tokyo established a sanitary engineering programme in the Urban Engineering Department as a half-size department. In 1968, the University of Osaka established the first Department of Environmental Engineering in Japan. Until that time, two forerunners, the Universities of Hokkaido and Kyoto, expanded their programmes from classic sanitary engineering to environmental engineering studies. Today, the names of the two departments are the Department of Sanitary and Environmental Engineering and the Department of Environmental and Sanitary Engineering respectively.

In the 1990s, the period of global environmental issues, several new faculties have been established, such as the Graduate School of Environmental Information Science at Keio University and the Graduate School of Environmental Earth Science at Hokkaido University.

During the same period, Japanese major national universities have been reforming their organisation from ordinary university to graduate research university status. Among the engineering schools, the Universities of Tokyo and Kyoto started the reformation in 1993 and the Universities of Hokkaido, Nagoya and Tohoku followed in 1994. In these transformations, environmental engineering education programmes and research systems have also changed. The cases of Hokkaido and Kyoto Universities will be explained in a later section.

In the coming century, an independent classic environmental engineering programme will not exist, but all engineering education will link with various environmental issues and include environmental aspects. Modern physical ways of thinking, which was once the leading philosophy of engineering science, cannot stand by themselves. Environmental issues should always be built into engineering studies. So-called classic environmental engineering will be absorbed in social engineering, which is based on natural ecological sciences and new social philosophy.

Today's Environmental Engineering Studies in Major Japanese National Universities

In Table 1 the name and size of environmental engineering departments in major Japanese national universities are summarised, together with their years of establishment. Details of the departments mentioned in Table 1 follow.

Hokkaido University

The Department of Sanitary and Environmental Engineering was established in 1957 as the first of its kind for research and education in sanitary engineering science and technology in Japan. Since then, it has grown into the nation's largest department of environmental engineering by adding new research and educational specialities to keep pace with the increasing number of environmental issues. The present activities of the department cover the latest developments in environmental engineering and science as well as more established approaches to sanitary engineering.

The department has laboratories for both engineering process research and environmental analysis with a comprehensive selection of instruments and equipment. The department's computer also serves to facilitate the research and educational activities.

The Division of Sanitary Engineering in the Graduate School is operated in close coop-eration with the Graduate School of Environmental Earth Science.

Undergraduate Curriculum
Required Subjects

Introduction to Sanitary and Environmental Engineering, City Planning, Environmen-tal Health, Fluid Mechanics I & II, Thermodynamics and Heat-transfer I & II, Struc-tural Engineering I, Statistics for Environmental Engineers, Computer Programming and Numerical Analysis, Engineering Mathematics I & II, Principles of Analytical Chem-istry, Principles of Organic & Biochemistry, Principles of Physical Chemistry, Sanitary Engineering Design and Drawing, Graduation Thesis.

Elective Subjects (I)

Water Works Engineering I & II, Sewage Works Engineering I & II, Water Quality Science and Water Pollution Control I & II, Environmental Process Engineering I & II, Air Condition I & II, Urban Environmental Engineering I & II, Solid Wastes Control I & II, Air Pollution Control I & II.

Elective Subjects (II)

Fluid Transportation, Bio-meteorological Health Engineering, Structural Engineering II, Unit Operation for Sanitary Engineers I & II, Microbiology for Sanitary Engineers, Meteorology, Hydrology, Building Equipment I & II, Soil Mechanics, Environmental Chemistry Laboratory, Physics Laboratory, Sanitary and Environmental Engineering Laboratory I & II, Exercise in Sanitary and Environmental Engineering I & II, Biology and Ecology for Environmental Engineers, Introduction to Construction Engineering, Introduction to Nuclear Engineering, Introduction to Electrical Engineering, Introduc-tion to Electronics, Industrial Economics.

Name of Department and University	Year Established	Professors and Instructors	Number of Students per Year		
			BE 4 Years	MS 2 Years	PhD 3 Years
Sanitary & Environmental Engineering (Hokkaido)	1957	16 + (16)	55	16 + (X)	8
Environmental & Sanitary Engineering (Kyoto)	1958	12 + (12)	45	12 + (X)	7
Urban Engineering (Toyko)	1960	10 + (10)	20	8 + (X)	4
Environmental Engineering (Osaka)	1968	12 + (12)	45	12 + (X)	6

Table 1: *Major Japanese National University Environmental Engineering Departments.*

Graduate Curriculum

<u>Master's Course</u> (All subjects are elective)

Regional Aqua System Planning, Advanced Water Treatment, Advanced Fluid Transportation Engineering, Advanced Water and Wastewater Treatment System Planning, Advanced Water Quality Science and Control, Advanced Environmental Bioengineering, Advanced Environmental Engineering Systems, Advanced Thermo-Environmental Engineering Design, Advanced Air Conditioning, Advanced Human Environmental Engineering, Advanced Urban Environmental Planning, Environmental Risk Management, Waste Incineration Engineering, Solid Waste Landfill Engineering, Advanced Environmental Physiology, Advanced Environmental meteorology, Advanced Environmental Statistics, Advanced Applied Mathematics I, Exercise on Advanced Applied Mathematics, Advanced Seminar on Sanitary Engineering I, II & III, Advanced Exercise on Sanitary Engineering I, II, III & IV.

<u>Doctor's Course</u>

Advanced Topics in Sanitary and Environmental Engineering I, II & III

The above mentioned programmes are carried out by professors belonging to the engineering laboratories of water works, sewage works, water quality management, thermal environment, environmental process, solid wastes control, urban environment and air pollution control.

Kyoto University

The Department of Environmental & Sanitary Engineering was established in 1958 separate from the sanitary engineering section of the Civil Engineering Department, and has developed a highly interdisciplinary character in order to address the wide scope of environmental engineering problems. The emphasis of the department is presently placed on the development of the scientific and engineering principles and methods required to solve various problems in water supply and sewerage works, water pollution control, solid waste management, air pollution control, noise control, radiological health and micropollutant control.

The Department encompasses four related fields having separate research facilities, including the Laboratory for Control of Environmental Micropollutants (Otsu City), the Research Section for Radioactive Waste Management at the Research Reactor Institute (Osaka Pref), the Research Section for Radiological Health and Safety at the Institute of Atomic Energy (Uji City), and the Environmental Preservation Center (Main Campus).

Undergraduate Curriculum

<u>Sophomore</u>

Introduction to Environmental and Sanitary Engineering, Applied Mathematics for Environmental and Sanitary Engineering, Computer Programming in Environmental and Sanitary Engineering.

Junior

Environmental Health, Transport Phenomena, Environmental Plant Engineering, Environmental System Engineering, Atmospheric Environment, Air Pollution, Water Quality, Water Pollution Control, Water Collection and Distribution Engineering, Water Supply and Sewerage, Radiological Health Engineering, Waste Management Engineering, Environmental and Sanitary Engineering Laboratory I, II & III, Seminar in Environmental and Sanitary Engineering I, *Structural Mechanics I & Exercises (CVL), *Fluid Mechanics and Hydraulics & Exercises (CVL), *Construction Materials (CVL), *River Hydrology (CVL), *Basic Biochemistry I (ICH), *Physical Chemistry B I (FDC), *Engineering Mathematics B I a (CVL), *Engineering Mathematics I b (CVL), *Engineering Mechanics I B (CVL), *Engineering Mathematics B II (CVL).

Senior

Public Health, Environmental Statistics, Industrial Waste Treatment, Global Environmental Engineering, Design Exercise for Environmental Facilities, Seminar in Environmental & Sanitary Engineering II, *Soil Mechanics & Exercises (CVL), *Theory of Planning in Civil Engineering System & Exercises (CVL), *Urban & Regional Planning (CVL), *Water Resource Engineering (CVL), *Basic Biochemistry II (ICH), *Process Systems Engineering I (CHE), *Process Systems Engineering II (CHE), *Physical Chemistry B I (FDC), Graduation Research Work.

Graduate Curriculum
Environmental Planning and Modelling, Environmental Transport Phenomena, Environmental System Engineering Adv., Air Pollution Adv., Noise Control, Environmental Microbiology, Microbiology for Water Supply, Water Quality Control Engineering Adv., Water Pollution Control Adv., Control of Environmental Radiation, Treatment of Radioactive Wastes, Aerosol Science, Global Environmental Engineering Adv., Solid Wastes and Waste Water Treatment Adv., Laboratory & Seminar in Environmental and Sanitary Engineering Adv., *Metropolitan Planning (CVL), *River Engineering Adv. (CVL), *Planning in Civil Engineering System Adv. (CVL), *Water Resources Systems Analysis (CVL), *Field Mechanics & Hydraulics Adv. (CVL), *Public Economics (ECO), *Engineering Mathematics Adv. I (AMP), *Engineering Mathematics Adv. II (AMP), *Engineering Mechanics Adv. (AMP), *Advanced Process Systems Engineering (CHE), *Advanced Chemical Process Control (CHE), *Chemical Reaction Engineering (CHE), Master's Thesis.

*Given by university members of other divisions. CVL: Civil Engineering; CHE: Chemical Engineering; AMP: Applied Mathematics and Physics; ECO: Faculty of Economics.

Tokyo University

The Department of Urban Engineering started even before urban problems became a serious public concern. Independent proposals for the Department of Sanitary Engineering in 1958 and for the Department for Urban Planning in 1960 were integrated, and the Department of Urban Engineering was established in 1962.

The aim of the department is to give students a background in the planning, design and management of the urban community. The programmes offered here are designed to help meet the widespread needs for specially-educated manpower in urban planning and environmental engineering. The department is composed of urban planning courses, with a strong emphasis being placed on studio and/or laboratory work. In addition, INTEP (International Environmental Planning Center) was established in the department to educate on international cooperation for environmental management.

(1) Urban Planning Course

The aim of the course is to train students as physical planners who have a comprehensive knowledge and an ability in the various engineering fields required for urban planning, such as civil engineering, architecture and building science, environmental engineering, social science and data analysis. Unique studio work is provided in which the students learn how to design building complexes, individual communities and regions. The studio work includes collection of urban data, analysis of the collected data, projections of urban structures and construction of physical models.

(2) Environmental and Sanitary Engineering Course

Environmental and sanitary engineers are responsible for controlling and managing water, air, solid waste and land resources and for preserving the quality of urban environments. The students take studio work such as the design of water or wastewater treatment plants and environmental protection, and laboratory research such as water quality analysis, field surveys for environmental pollution control, and experiments on hydrodynamics and water treatment.

Osaka University

The aim of the Department of Environmental Engineering is to provide students with the ability to remove environmental hazards, preserve the environment, and create a new environment based on an extensive and deep understanding of human society, nature, ecosystems, and resources in each spatial level — dwelling, city and region. Since environmental problems are interdisciplinary in nature, education is conducted in cooperation with many other departments. Much research work is done by imaginatively adapting the traditional methodologies in order to attain new scientific paradigms for the analysis, planning and design of the environment.

Graduates of the department play an active part in the planning and execution of environmental work in a large number of fields, such as government offices, local self-governing bodies, public corporations, construction companies, and so on.

The aim of the graduate course in Environmental Engineering is to produce specialists in environmental engineering with an extensive and deep understanding of human society, nature, ecosystems, resources, etc. Since environmental problems are interdisciplinary in nature, education and research in this course covers many fields. Many research projects have been, and are being, carried out to improve the present environment and to create a better environment for the future. In the early formative years, research work was based on traditional disciplines, but they are now interdisciplinary in their frequent re-evaluation of urban developments and environmental problems in

Japan. All of the research currently in progress seeks to attain new scientific paradigms for the analysis, planning and design of environments.

Undergraduate Curriculum

Required Subjects

Principles of Environment, Theory of Living Environment, Urban Design, Environmental design I & II, Environmental Thermal Engineering I & II, Fluid Mechanics I & II, Environmental Chemistry I & II, Water Resources Engineering, Environmental Hydrology and Hydraulics, Experiments in Environmental Engineering, Environmental Design Studio I & II, Exercises in Environmental Design and Engineering I & II, Thesis Work.

Elective Subjects

Mathematical Analysis I, II, III & IV, Mechanics, Probability and Statistics, Introduction to Strength of Materials and Machine Design, Analytical Chemistry I, Outline of Chemical Engineering, Introduction to Electric Engineering, Traffic Engineering, Introductory Mathematics for Environmental Engineers, Numerical Analysis, Exercises in Information Processing I & II, City and Regional Planning, Planning of Residential Area, Introduction to Architecture, Environmental Thermal Engineering III, Air Conditioning, Fluid Mechanics III, Air Purification, Water Conservation Engineering I & II, Theory of Environmental Systems Analysis and Planning, Regional Resources Management, Urban Renewal, Structural Planning of Buildings, Building Administration, Disaster Prevention Engineering, Landscape Architecture, Environmental Installation Engineering, Theory of Energy, Meteorology, Environmental Genetics, Environmental Biology, Environmental Medicine, Environmental Acoustics, Environmental Policy, Environmental Economics.

Graduate Curriculum

Human Settlement (Advanced), Regional Planning (Advanced), Environmental Design (Advanced), Systematic Design Method, Environmental Thermal Engineering (Advanced), Planning of Air-Conditioning (Advanced), Atmospheric Diffusion, Air Purification (Advanced), Environmental Chemistry (Advanced), Water conservation Engineering (Advanced), Dynamics and Economics for Water and Environmental Resources Management, Theory of Environmental Planning Exercises in Advanced Environmental Engineering I, II, III & IV, Exercises in Environmental Engineering, Seminar on Environmental Engineering I & II, Applied Mathematics I & II, Mathematical Statistics, Special Topics I & II.

Change to Graduate Research Universities

The engineering schools of major national universities are reorganising as graduate research schools. This means that all faculties and research laboratories are in the graduate school. The graduate school hangs overshadows undergraduate study programmes. The undergraduate school becomes a purely educational organization and the programme is oriented toward the basics.

Each university has its own policy for reorganising conventional university systems. Kyoto University is reforming its system by adopting a single, very large undergraduate department while maintaining ordinary size graduate divisions. For example, the former civil, traffic, environmental and sanitary and the resource development engineering departments are being reorganized into one big department dealing with all aspects of engineering. However, graduate divisions are nearly the same as today's.

In Hokkaido University, the system is quite new. Undergraduate departments are not greatly different in classification, but the curricula are turned into very fundamental ones and cooperate with neighbour departments. The graduate school is organized with 42 laboratories and educational programmes from today's divisions (departments). Each laboratory consists of 3 to 4 full professors and 3 to 4 associate professors with 4 to 5 instructors, operating one compulsory study programme of 8 to 10 credits. Students must take two study programmes for a ME (major speciality and minor). They must carry out their thesis work and seminars in their major laboratory. In the system, the Graduate Engineering School of Hokkaido University has, theoretically, about 900 optional combination curricula for ME degrees. For PhD degrees, a third programme is taken.

With respect to environmental engineering graduate research and education, five research groups, each with compulsory programmes such as urban environmental planning, human environmental planning, environmental sanitation, environmental conservation, waste management and recycling, have been established. These groups belong separately in the two divisions of urban environmental engineering and environmental resources engineering with the other five groups such as water resource engineering, mineral resource engineering, city planning, and transportation engineering. Hence, it is very easy for a student who wishes to take another programme proposed by a different division's group, such as information theory, computer science, database engineering, system analysis, atomic energy systems, applied nuclear science, fluid mechanics, thermodynamics, process control, aquatic chemistry, etc. By this very flexible combination, environmental engineering curricula will have a wide span and sharpness. We call this a π–shape curriculum.

In addition, Hokkaido University established the Graduate School of Environmental Earth Science in 1992. This faculty has three divisions — Geoscience, Bioscience and Material Science. The division of Geoscience consists of laboratories of geoecology, geosphere science, cryosphere science and snow and ice science. The division of Bioscience consists of laboratories of regional ecosystems, environmental medicine and informatics, bio-material chemistry, ecology and genetics, environmental molecular biology, cytogenetics and adaptation biology. The division of Material Science consists of molecular functional chemistry, advanced material chemistry, organic chemistry, molecular photochemistry and catalytic science.

The environmental groups in the engineering school have many cooperative research and study programmes.

Conclusion

For the next century, a fixed environmental engineering education is not possible. All engineering divisions should connect with core environmental programmes to work through the environmental age. The core programmes cannot stand alone, but must connect with many programmes in other environmental science, social engineering and production engineering programmes.

Malaysia

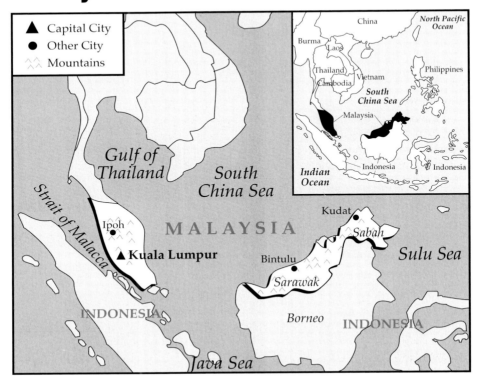

The country of Malaysia consists of two regions separated by the South China Sea. The first part, Peninsular Malaya, occupies most of the Malay Peninsula and is adjacent to Thailand. The second part, Sarawak and Sabah, lies on the northern coast of Borneo, 650 kilometres from Peninsular Malaya. Together, the regions total 330,000 square kilometres.

The population of Malaysia totals about 18.5 million people, about 60% of which live in rural areas. Eighty percent of the population live in Peninsular Malaya. The capital city, Kuala Lumpur, is the country's largest and has about 1.2 million people.

The Malay economy depends heavily on the production of petroleum, rubber, timber and tin.

Much of Malaysia is mountainous and covered in rainforest. The rainforests contain one of the world's most diverse ecosystems, and many rare species.

Education is free for children between the ages of 6 and 19. Malaysia has seven universities, including the University of Malaya in Kuala Lumpur, the University of Technology Malaysia, the University of Agriculture Malaysia and the University of Science in Penang. Other tertiary institutions include institutes of technology, polytechnics and teacher training colleges.

Environmental Engineering Education in Malaysia

M A Hashim
Institute for Advanced Studies
University of Malaya
Kuala Lumpur, Malaysia

Abstract

In recent years, various institutions of higher learning in Malaysia have incorporated environmental engineering in the education and training of engineers. However, environmental engineering at the undergraduate level is not usually presented as a separate discipline. Most of the subject matter in environmental engineering is offered by civil and chemical engineering departments. At the postgraduate level, various universities offer masters and doctoral programmes in environmental science and engineering. In addition, external courses for postgraduate study in environmental management are being introduced for suitably qualified professionals. These programmes, conducted in collaboration with foreign universities, are aimed at the needs of managers, government officers, engineers, scientists and other professionals who are involved in the planning and implementation of environmental projects and policies.

Introduction

Industrialisation, rising standards of living and the exploitation of new materials and energy sources are characteristic of mankind's progress. Unfortunately, in many ways these are also a source of new problems such as overpopulation, the energy crisis and environmental quality degradation. In particular, in today's environmentally conscious society, the problem of pollution has gained full-fledged public recognition. Well-known environmental tragedies like mercury poisoning in Minamata Bay in Japan, the massive oil spill caused by the Exxon Valdez incident, methylisocyanate poisoning at Bhopal and acid rain in the Scandinavian countries have reinforced our society's perception that the quality of the environment is being seriously degraded.

The sociocultural roots of our present environmental crisis lie in the paradigms of scientific materialism and economic determinism, which fail to recognise the physical limits imposed by ecological systems on economic activity. The economies have to expand within ecosystems that have limited regenerative capacity. Contrary to the neoclassical theory of continuous material growth, economic activities directly undermine the potential for development through over-exploitation of natural resources and indirectly compromise future production through discharge of residuals.

For a developing country like Malaysia, it is now generally recognised that environmental management, sustainable development and economic growth are inextricably interlinked and that the relationships are extremely complex. These interrelationships have to be understood for a proper appreciation of the issues involved in the integration of environment with development. The ultimate goal for Malaysia is to have rapid economic development without environmental degradation.

This goal can most probably be realised through modification of the present engineering education system. This is because engineers are directly involved in creating facilities and utilities for industrialisation, transportation and communications. Most of these engineering activities have created wealth, but at the same time have resulted in massive ecological problems in the form of deforestation, atmospheric pollution, surface and ground water pollution and soil erosion (Aziz 1990). It has become increasingly clear to the engineering community that engineers should be educated to appreciate the adverse impact of engineering activities on the environment. This environmental aspect has not been emphasised in the early engineering education system. It is perhaps not too late for the present engineering education system to produce engineers who are technically competent as well as environmentally conscious.

As a first step, the Malaysian government has introduced basic environmental education at all levels of the education system. The aim of these programmes is to inculcate students with attitudes and values that will promote awareness and sensitivity to environmental protection and conservation. At the tertiary level, environmental education for professional development is being offered by public institutions of higher learning. The major aim of this paper is to examine the current status of environmental education in Malaysia with special emphasis on environmental education for engineers. Before discussing the structure of environmental engineering education in Malaysia, it is useful to give a brief account of the approaches adopted by the Malaysian government to tackle the environmental problems associated with rapid economic development.

Economic Development and Environmental Management in Malaysia

The last two decades have seen tremendous progress and unprecedented development in Malaysia. Malaysia's average annual rate of economic growth of 7.8% during the 1970s and about 6% during the 1980s reflected a sound and growing economy and a high degree of success with its developmental strategy and planning. Within the overall growth-oriented macro-economic framework, the stress was on poverty eradication. Poverty eradication in the rural sector entailed large-scale and rapid clearing of forests on the one hand, and on the other hand by in-situ development that included, among other features, the granting of subsidies for the purchase of pesticides and fertilisers by the farmers. In the urban sector, poverty eradication entailed a rapid creation of jobs through a quickened pace of industrialisation and infrastructural development. All these measures led to the attainment of rapid economic growth and a considerable reduction in the incidence of poverty in both rural and urban areas. These activities also led to social costs, as manifested in resource depletion, soil erosion and the generation of various forms of pollution, including toxic and hazardous wastes. Rapid urbanisation coupled with an encouragement to rely on private, rather than public, transport led to the worsening of traffic congestion and air pollution in urban areas.

Awareness of environmental issues has been growing at different levels during the past 20 years in Malaysia. Following the 1972 United Nations Conference on the Human Environment in Stockholm, the Environmental Quality Act was passed in 1974, and the Division of Environment (DOE) was set up in 1975 to administer the Act. Since then, the DOE has grown into a department supported by eight regional offices throughout the country (DOE 1988). In addition to the DOE, the Malaysian government set up a National Council for Environment (NCE) to coordinate the functioning of all agencies, consider strategies and programmes that have implications on the environment and advise the government on policies leading towards a more holistic approach to environmental management.

Malaysia's rapid economic development has relied heavily on its natural resources, ranging from forestry, land and water to fossil fuels and minerals. This rapid development has resulted in air and water pollution, noise pollution, and solid and hazardous wastes, which are of serious concern in certain areas in Malaysia. In order to sustain rapid economic growth, the Malaysian government, through the DOE and other environment-related agencies, has adopted environmental management strategies and programmes that are comprehensive and yet pragmatic in its continuing efforts to strike a balance between the goals of economic development and environmental protection. Concern for environmental quality has, thus, gained considerable momentum in recent years in Malaysia.

The Malaysian government has also made many efforts in collaboration with universities, professional engineering bodies and voluntary organisations to disseminate information on environmental issues through lectures, seminars and workshops to the general public. Various public educational institutions and government departments in Malaysia have conducted workshops, seminars and short-term courses on environmental issues. Between 1986 and 1990, the National Institute of Public Administration (INTAN) provided training to a large number of public sector personnel in various fields, including environmental management.

The Malaysian government has adopted a national policy on sustainable economic development that incorporates environmental considerations into developmental activities. A natural resource conservation strategy to maintain essential ecological processes, ensure genetic diversity and prevent environmental quality degradation is also being actively pursued. The Malaysian government's effort to strengthen educational programmes for environmental manpower development is discussed below.

Environmental Engineering Education in Malaysia

In recent years the government of Malaysia has included environmental education at all levels of the education system. These environmental education programmes are aimed at creating general awareness and a sense of responsibility towards the environment among the educated. The primary school curriculum provides continuous and liberal inputs of environmental concerns and is built around themes like the interaction of man with the environment, man and the biosphere, the interaction of the elements in the environment and issues related to man and the environment. At the secondary school level, the syllabus includes many topics that have direct bearing on environmental issues. For example, school children are taught to monitor acid rain levels and to take part in problem-solving projects related to environmental issues, such as solid waste disposal and air pollution control.

At the tertiary level, the objective of environmental engineering education is to produce professionals who are well-versed in the sciences, engineering and management of the environment. In the last decade, considerable progress has been made in this area. Many courses were added to the curriculum of undergraduate programmes in civil and chemical engineering. Master degree programmes were also introduced in some universities, such as the National University of Malaysia (UKM) and the University of Science Malaysia (USM).

In the civil engineering undergraduate curriculum, an introductory course on environmental studies is offered in the first year. This course deals with the concept of basic ecology, man and the ecosystem, natural resources and their utilisation and the technology-society-environment interface (Abllah, 1988). The impacts of human activities on the environment and the control and legislative issues for environmental protection in Malaysia are major components of this course. Ecological principles in terms of biogeochemical cycles are also included. The course on "Engineer in Society" in the second year civil engineering undergraduate programme deals with human relations, economic requirements and social, environmental and political factors.

In the third year, conservation issues are highlighted and the importance of harmony between technology and the environment is stressed. The course on conservation also deals with the natural equilibrium in different ecosystems and the interference by human activities on the ecological equilibrium. Traditional courses in civil engineering such as public health engineering, hydraulics and water resource engineering are offered in the third and fourth year. Optional courses in environmental engineering include advanced hydraulics, water resources management and advanced hydrology. These are advanced courses that deal with unit operations and processes for water, waste water and solid waste treatment and management. In addition to treatment technology, effluent reuse and reclamation aspects are also covered. Environmental management is another important area of specialisation in the undergraduate civil engineering curriculum. In this course, technologies related to clean water, fertile land, clean air, modern housing and healthy life are emphasised.

The chemical engineering undergraduate programme includes a course on industrial waste water treatment using physical, chemical and biological methods. Biological waste treatment technology is also emphasised in the optional biochemical engineering course. Traditional courses in chemical engineering (such as heat and mass transfer, transport phenomena, process control, reactor design and separation processes) are directly relevant to the technical aspects of environmental engineering. Some of these courses are being modified to stress their relevance to environmental engineering.

Basic science subjects, such as analytical chemistry, ecology and microbiology, and environmental subjects like pollution prevention, waste minimisation, low waste or no-waste technologies, environmental impact assessment, environmental audit, risk and hazard analysis and disaster management, are being developed into optional courses in the chemical engineering undergraduate curriculum (Sulaiman, 1990). Ideally, these subjects should be included in a comprehensive environmental engineering programme. Unfortunately, the present chemical engineering curriculum is not able to accommodate all these courses because the programme is already overloaded with compulsory courses. Perhaps the time has arrived for the engineering community in Malaysia to consider environmental engineering as a separate undergraduate discipline.

Postgraduate programmes in environmental science and engineering are being offered by different universities in Malaysia. These programmes include basic science courses such as environmental chemistry, biology, microbiology and ecology, engineering courses such as industrial waste treatment, air pollution control, solid waste management, water and waste water engineering, and management courses such as environmental management, disaster management and resource management. The aim of these programmes is to train engineers and scientists and to give them the specialised knowledge and skills to solve environmental problems.

The latest development in environmental engineering education in Malaysia is that private organisations, such as the Environmental Management and Research Association of Malaysia (ENSEARCH), are conducting Master of Environmental Management (MEM) programmes in collaboration with foreign universities. ENSEARCH has developed the programme as part of its contribution to the nation's technological development in environmental protection and enhancement. These programmes offer opportunities to practising professionals to upgrade their environmental knowledge, skills and capabilities. The main objective of the programmes is to lay the foundation for training professionals who will have the technical knowledge and capability to protect and enhance the environment.

In conclusion, both public education organisations and private professional bodies in Malaysia are making serious efforts to equip new and practising engineers with environmental knowledge and skills, as the activities of this group of professionals have the greatest influence on the environment.

References
Abllah, N F B N (1988). "Civil Engineering Education". *Proceedings AEESEAP Regional Conference on Engineering Education.* Kuala Lumpur, Malaysia.

Aziz, M A (1990). "Environmental Aspects of Engineering Education". *Proceedings AEESEAP/FEISEAP International Conference on Engineering Education.* Penang, Malaysia.

DOE (1988). *Environmental Perspective to the Year 2000 and Beyond.* Workshop on Sustainable Development, Department of Environment, Kuala Lumpur, Malaysia.

Sulaiman, N M N (1990). "The 'Greening' of Chemical Engineering Education". *Proceedings Symposium of Malaysian Chemical Engineers.* Universiti Teknologi Malaysia, Kuala Lumpur, Malaysia.

Papua New Guinea

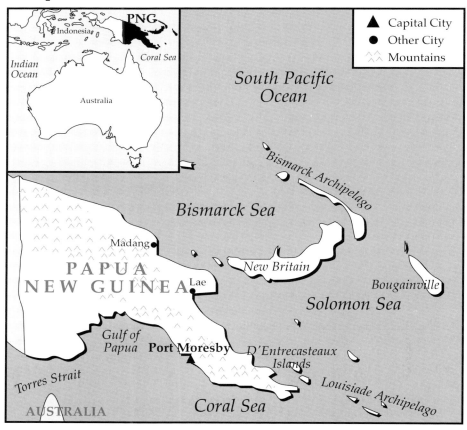

Papua New Guinea lies in the Pacific Ocean north of Australia. It occupies the eastern half of the island of New Guinea and includes the Bismarck Archipelago, the northern part of the Solomon Islands and numerous small islands. Papua New Guinea's total area is 460,000 km^2 and the population of 3.6 million is distributed unevenly throughout the country.

Most of Papua New Guinea has a hot, humid climate and rainfall averages about 250 cm a year. Papua New Guinea has abundant natural resources, and the economy is based on farming and forestry. Most people grow their own food and obtain other necessities from the forests. Copper is mined on the island of Bougainville and other products include coffee, cocoa, timber and fish.

Education is not compulsory in Papua New Guinea. About 60 percent of children attend primary school and about 15 percent of these go on to secondary education. Other students attend vocational schools and specialist training is available at various colleges. The University of Papua New Guinea at Port Moresby was established in 1966, and the University of Technology at Lae offers degrees and diplomas in technical fields.

Developments in Environmental Engineering Education
in Papua New Guinea

G K N S Subasinghe and S Bordia
Department of Mining Engineering
Papua New Guinea University of Technology
Lae, Papua New Guinea

Abstract

Environmental education is an essential component in the training of young professionals. In Papua New Guinea, the need for such courses has arisen due to the increasing impact of development projects on the environment. Tertiary institutions have responded to this national need by introducing environmental science-related courses into the curricula. This paper describes the development of such courses, their limitations and the possible remedies to overcome these limitations, especially with regard to environmental education for engineers.

Introduction

Papua New Guinea is the largest island nation in the Pacific and is extremely rich in flora and fauna. It comprises the eastern half of the subcontinental island of New Guinea and the islands of the Bismarck Archipelago, as well as some 600 smaller islands, and encompasses a total area of 465,000 square kilometres. The interior of both the mainland and provincial islands are fragmented and mountainous, with extensive areas of flat and gentle terrain in the coastal areas. The combinations of topography, geology, climate and volcanic events has created a complex pattern of soils, some of which are very productive. Large river systems rise in the mountain regions and a large portion of the highland areas is covered by tropical rain forests.

Papua New Guinea is very rich in natural resources. Many rare and endangered birds, a wide variety of mammals and an estimated 9000 species of plants and trees occupy its varied environments. Part of the rich diversity of PNG is its people, who still own almost all its land and are highly dependent on it for their way of life. Protection of the environment and conservation of its rich diversity of species is necessary to protect the culture of the people. Management and conservation of the environment cannot be successful without an understanding of the needs of the people and their cooperation (DEC, 1992).

The government has recognised its responsibility to maintain and, where possible, improve the quality of the environment during its development of Papua New Guinea. This fact is borne out by the fourth of the five goals of the country's constitution on natural resources and environment (OEC, 1976), which states:

> *"We declare our fourth goal to be for PNG's natural resources and environment to be conserved and used for the collective benefit of us all, and be replenished for the benefit of future generations."*

Environmental Impacts and Development Trends

Current development trends in PNG are focused mainly on the areas of minerals and energy, agriculture, forestry, fisheries and marine resources and urban and infrastructural development.

Exploration for, and development of, large mineral and petroleum resources have substantial local impacts on the physical and social environment. Such development projects require trained professionals in planning, implementation and assessment of environmental management schemes. Increasing agricultural production is one of the main aims of the government's development plans, but soil erosion needs careful management in such projects due to the high rainfall over much of the country.

Due to recent adverse publicity about its activities, there has been considerable concern in the logging industry over the implementation of new structures and legislation for the management and protection of forests as a renewable natural resource. In order to ensure the protection of the ecosystem, alternative schemes to harvest the forests by less damaging means have been the focus of attention in recent times.

Marine and freshwater products play an important role in subsistence and local trade. The water quality of river systems may be adversely affected by mining and soil erosion, creating a threat to the sustainable management of fisheries and welfare of the communities that depend on this resource.

Due to population growth, the government is committed to the provision of infrastructural and urban development. Even though the urban population is comparatively small in this country, the above developments require controlled measures to reduce the overall impact on the environment.

The development of renewable and non-renewable resources has significant implications for environmental management and presents a major challenge to the young engineers who plan, implement and execute such work.

Environmental Education in PNG

The natural environment has always been of enormous importance to the people of PNG. Only 11% of the total population live in towns and 75% are engaged in subsistence agriculture, depending directly on the natural environment for survival. Development projects to date have all been based on the country's rich natural resources — the minerals, forests, water, land and wildlife. Large-scale development projects, notably the Bougainville copper mine, Ok Tedi mine, Porgera gold mine and the oil palm industry, have highlighted the environmental problems of development. Forestry, agro-industry, hydroelectricity, roads, fisheries, livestock, tourism and industrial and urban management projects also require consideration of environmental issues and understanding of the interacting components of the systems in which they occur.

Developments in environmental education in PNG have, therefore, taken place alongside the increasing concern over the impacts of development on the environment, and a recognised need for informed decision-makers and a public that can participate in decisions that relate to the environment and development. The University of Papua New Guinea (UPNG) was the first to introduce courses in environmental science to cater for such demand, but environmental education spanning all disciplines has not come about for a number of reasons, including staff and funding shortages. The environmental science programme at the UPNG was initiated in 1980 as a direct response to demands for environmentally-aware graduates. It was envisaged as a programme that would have the interdisciplinary and multidisciplinary approach that is necessary for the understanding of complex environmental issues. The programme is available to students of any discipline and provides a secondary specialisation relevant to the main subject studied. The main objectives (King, 1989) of this programme were to:

- look at environmental issues from a wide range of view points; and

- train graduates able to communicate with a wide range of specialists concerned with environmental management.

The programme was given a multidisciplinary nature by incorporating representatives from each department of the science faculty (i.e. biology, physics, chemistry, agriculture and geology), from the departments of anthropology and sociology, economics and geography, and the faculties of medicine and law in its organising committee.

The final year of the four-year Environmental Sciences Programme was offered for the first time in 1983. In its first two years, a series of evening seminars concentrating on multidisciplinary approaches to environmental issues were held. These attracted a wide audience of students and the general public, but were discontinued in 1984. The seminars were published in two environmental education texts (Chambers and Eaton, 1982,1983).

The first two years of the course offer an introduction to physical environmental processes and an examination of the structure and functioning of biological systems. In year three, resources-based courses are offered, which provide a description and understanding of the biotic, energy, water, human, mineral and land resources of PNG. In the final year, more emphasis is given to environmental management, together with a consideration of economic, social, legal and political needs, and includes field visits to major development and nature conservation projects (UPNG, 1993).

Considering the small percentage of university students who undertake courses in environmental science programmes, a growing emphasis has been directed towards incorporating environmental education into other major areas of study. These include courses conducted by the faculties of art, science, law, medicine and education. Within the Faculty of Education, there are programmes of initial teacher education, graduate teacher education and degree or postgraduate in-service teacher education. Such programmes incorporate a broad background knowledge of the environment and environmental issues and relate to topics found in existing community school and provincial high school syllabi. These syllabi have been revised to include environmental education at all levels of the curriculum.

Goroka Teacher's College, which is part of the UPNG, trains teachers in a wide variety of subjects. Of these, science and social science courses incorporate a certain amount of environmental education in line with the high school syllabus.

Over the years, the UPNG, and in particular the science faculty, has undertaken research and consultancy projects that relate to environmental problems and the impact of development on the environment of PNG. Many such projects have directly involved students in the survey work, and data collected is often used for teaching purposes. Such "on-the-job" training opportunities have been invaluable in educating senior students in real-life situations.

The university, through its links with the Association of South Pacific Environmental Institutions (ASPEI), assists in the implementation of the South Pacific Regional Environmental Programme (SPREP) work plan. It is also involved in the production of "Ples", an environmental education journal, which is distributed throughout the region to schools, government departments and community groups (King, 1989).

Environmental Education for Engineers

Engineers are expected not only to be aware of environmental concerns, but also to take a leading role in monitoring and assessing the environmental impacts arising from development work. Traditionally, the monitoring and assessments are carried out by science graduates and/or applied chemists. However, due to the lack of sufficiently qualified personnel in environmental science and engineering (particularly in developing countries such as PNG), site engineers are being required to carry out the monitoring work. This demands a fair knowledge and a grasp of the nature of the processes taking place in the surrounding environment. It is, therefore, essential that the engineers are given a general introduction to biological and physical processes in environmental systems, including analytical methods, to perform the above tasks.

Papua New Guinea University of Technology (PNGUT, 1981) has recognised the need for environmental education for engineers, particularly in the light of mining and urban developments, and has responded by including environmental engineering subjects, albeit limited in context and topics, in its civil engineering curriculum. More recently, this has been extended into the mining and mineral processing curriculum. The civil engineering curriculum includes two one-semester courses on environmental engineering in the final year. The first course concentrates on hydrology, ground water, storm water and sewage management, while the second had been based on topics in public health engineering, such as sanitation, water treatment, sewage treatment, solid and hazardous waste management etc. More recently (PNGUT, 1994) other topics such as air and noise pollution have been added to the second semester course, which is an elective subject.

At PNGUT, mineral technology was first introduced as one of two sections in the then-Department of Chemical Technology (the other section being food technology). With the introduction of Applied Chemistry as a third section in 1981, environmental science courses were introduced. The environmental science-related courses (i.e. water analysis, environmental science and environmental chemistry) are taught to applied chemistry undergraduates at the third and fourth year level. The courses are aimed at giving students an in-depth knowledge of measurement, monitoring and environmental impact assessment techniques, covering areas of water pollution, trace metal detection, soil degradation and ecotoxicology. The mineral technology students also took some of these courses and, in addition, essential components of environmental science were also covered in hydrometallurgy, such as tailings and mine waste disposal, toxic chemical neutralisation and disposal (PNGUT, 1981). Once the mineral technology stream moved into the newly-established Department of Mining Engineering, the intake of students has been through the foundation year in engineering, along with their mining engineering counterparts. From 1994 (PNGUT, 1994), in addition to a semester course in environmental engineering, a common course on mine environmental management will be introduced.

It has been recognised, however, that while these engineering students undertake some aspects of environmental engineering, the scope of their knowledge is limited.

In 1991, the Applied Sciences Department in PNGUT (with support from the International Development Program of Australian Universities and Colleges) investigated the possibility of establishing a degree stream in Environmental Sciences at PNGUT to supplement the course conducted at the UPNG. However, it was reported (Brown and Hawker, 1991) that the preferred option would be to establish, as a starting point, a postgraduate diploma course incorporating many of the environmentally-based courses already available at PNGUT, with a core of integrating subjects such as perspectives on relevant environmental topics, environmental administration policy and law, environmental impact assessment introduction to social science and negotiating skills. The main aim of this course is to produce environmentally-oriented graduates with the required analytical skills and multidisciplinary background to undertake demanding environmental monitoring and impact studies. Although a proposal based on the above was approved by the academic board of PNGUT, its implementation has been delayed due to budgetary constraints.

In the meantime, however, another proposal (PNGUT, 1993) to establish a National Environmental Research and Management Centre at PNGUT to administer the aspects of environmental education, research and management in PNG and other South Pacific island nations is also under consideration. The establishment of this centre is being actively pursued by the PNGUT and it is currently seeking the necessary funds and assistance from international and regional agencies such as UNESCO and SPREP. It is envisaged that this centre would provide the nucleus for developing the postgraduate diploma course in environmental science at this university and contribute greatly towards the more demanding environmental affairs in the region.

Shortfalls of Environmental Engineering Education at PNGUT

While some environmental engineering courses are being taught to civil and mineral engineering students in their third and final years, it is believed that the courses offered at present are inadequate for the graduates to confidently undertake environmental impact assessments. As many environmental problems and their solutions are multidisciplinary in nature, it has been recognised that it is not possible to adequately train engineers, in developing countries in particular, in sufficient detail that they could handle such problems on their own. This is because of the restrictions in resources available and the timeframe required for such training.

At PNGUT, the engineering departments do not offer an introductory course in chemistry, with the exception of the Department of Mining Engineering. This is a major shortfall in the current engineering curriculum. However, with more emphasis on environmental education for engineers, this situation is likely to be rectified in the future.

Generally, technological solutions to environmental problems may never be an adequate solution in PNG, particularly with some 95% of the country in private ownership. As has been demonstrated in the past, landowner groups have made excessive compensation claims in relation to the use of their lands in development projects, mainly due to misinformation and misconceptions arising from communication problems. Engineers have a major role in handling such matters and, therefore, some elements of social science, particularly negotiation skills, should also be included in the environmental engineering education curriculum.

Recommendations

In general, the environmental courses taught at present to engineering students in PNG are considered inadequate in preparing engineers to handle environmental problems, due to the multidisciplinary nature of the subject. To cover relevant topics in environmental engineering in greater detail, students should be exposed to subjects such as chemistry and biology at an introductory level. In PNG, as most environmental problems need not only technical solutions but also involve social considerations, some elements of the social sciences, particularly negotiating skills, need to be included in environmental engineering education curriculum at an early stage.

References

Brown, L and D Hawker (1991). Report submitted to International Development Programme of Australian Universities and Colleges, on *The Proposed Environmental Sciences Programme at the Papua New Guinea University of Technology* (unpublished).

Chambers, M P and P Eaton, eds. (1982). *Environmental Education Series*. Vol 1. Por Moresby: University of Papua New Guinea.

Chambers, M P and P Eaton, eds. (1983). *Environmental Education Series*. Vol 2. Port Moresby: University of Papua New Guinea.

Department of Environment and Conservation (1992). *Strategic Plan*. Waigani, Papua New Guinea.

King, B (1989). "Environmental Education at a general level in tertiary education in Papua New Guinea". *Proceedings UNESCO Sub-Regional Conference on Environmental Education*. Sydney, Australia.

Office of the Environment and Conservation (1976). Quoted from the Constitution of Papua New Guinea, in *Environment and Conservation Policy — A Statement of Principles*. Waigani, Papua New Guinea.

PNGUT (1981, 1994). *Course Handbooks*.

PNGUT (1993). Internal working paper on the Proposal for Papua New Guinea Environmental Research and Management Centre (unpublished).

University of Papua New Guinea (1993). *Handbook of Courses, Faculty of Arts*.

University of Papua New Guinea (1993). *Handbook of Courses, Faculty of Science*.

Singapore

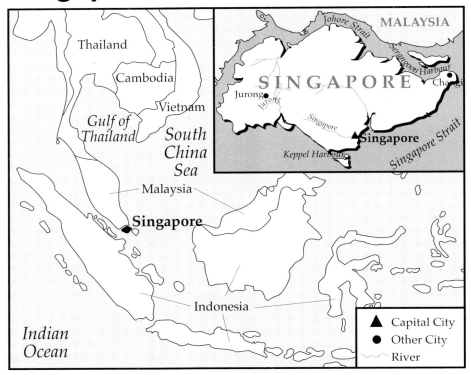

The small island country of Singapore lies at the southern end of the Malay Peninsula. One large island, also called Singapore, and more than 50 smaller islands make up Singapore's 618 square kilometres. Half of the smaller islands are uninhabited, and some have been developed for tourism and recreation. With a population of around 2.8 million, Singapore is one of the world's most densely populated countries. Most of the people live in the capital city of Singapore on the main island.

Singapore is highly urbanised. It is Southeast Asia's main port and an important financial, trade and transportation centre.

Rainforests once covered most of the main island, but most of this was cut down as trading developed. Tigers, wild boar and mousedeer have disappeared from Singapore's forests.

Rainfall in Singapore averages around 200 cm a year. Despite the plentiful rain, Singapore is not able to supply enough water to meet its needs, and imports water from Malaysia.

Singapore has one of the highest literacy rate in Southeast Asia. Children attend school from the age of six, and many finish secondary school. Tertiary education institutions include the National University of Singapore, the Nanyang Technological University and various polytechnics.

Environmental Engineering Education in Singapore

L C C Koe
Department of Civil Engineering
National University of Singapore
Singapore

Abstract

Environmental education in Singapore has been, and still continues to be, incorporated as part of the existing degree courses in civil and chemical engineering at the university level. This paper traces the initial introduction of environmental education in Singapore and provides some insights into its present status. The thinking behind the development of the need to provide increased emphasis on environmental education and the mechanism initiated to address this need is discussed.

Introduction

For more than three decades, the training of environmental engineers in Singapore has been incorporated into the curriculum of the Department of Civil Engineering at the National University of Singapore. In the early 1970s, the focus of environmental education was to ensure sufficient exposure and competence of civil engineering graduates in the relevant fields of water supply and pollution control, thus enabling our graduates to find employment with civil engineering companies involved in such environmental works. This strategy had served the nation well as the development of Singapore was then mainly concerned with the provision of water supply, waste facilities and associated sanitary works. The environmental topics selected, within the constraint of limited teaching hours allocated for environmental engineering subjects, were limited to lectures on hydrology, hydraulics, water supply, sewerage systems and waste treatment processes. To prepare students for these subjects, the fundamental topics of mathematics, mechanics and physics were considered adequate.

The current "buzz" words are now resource recovery, recycling and reuse. Environmental assessment is now a norm for large development projects and "sustainable development" is now feverishly pursued in all corners of the world. Environmental engineering concerns are now encompassing a wider area of interest, and ecosystems, public health and interaction of society with the environment now need to be addressed. There is also a growing emergence of friendly and cooperative management between the government and the industries to herald an image of what Singapore hopes to be, that is, an "Environment City". It is within this new world of cooperative environmental management that academia has to participate to ensure that appropriate technical manpower in environmental engineering be trained and are available for the nation's development.

Historical Background

When the engineering degree courses were initiated at the then-University of Singapore in the late 1960s, environmental engineering subjects, identified broadly as Environmental Engineering I and II, were incorporated into the civil engineering curriculum. With a total allocated lecture period of 100 hours, the two subjects introduced elemental topics such as hydrology, water supply, pipe networks, waste water treatment processes and selected presentations on water resources engineering. Offered in years 3 and 4 (the civil engineering degree course is of four years' duration), these subjects were complemented by laboratory classes on simple techniques of water analysis for fundamental pollution indicators, such as oxygen demand and suspended solids. While the civil engineering graduates cannot be considered environmental engineers, they were, nevertheless, equipped to participate in the planning, design and the construction of environmental facilities such as sewerage systems and water supply and treatment plants. At best, the graduates may be considered to be civil engineers with reasonable exposure to environmental engineering principles. The opportunities to specialise in advanced areas of environmental engineering were then limited and largely available through employment at the government's Ministry of the Environment.

In the mid-1980s, an attempt was made to incorporate new environmental topics into the environmental engineering curricula. This was carried out mainly via the introduction of subjects such as air pollution, advanced topics in waste treatment and environmental modelling. Because of the need to constrain such environmental subjects to not more than about 6% of the total lecture hours in the civil engineering courses, these subjects were introduced as options for the courses. The fundamental education of environmental engineers continued to be focused on hydrology and sanitary engineering. At the postgraduate level, advanced environmental subjects on water quality management, urban environmental management, industrial waste water control and environmental health were introduced.

To provide further opportunities for students in the environmental area, undergraduate studies in chemistry, reaction kinetics, chemical processes, transport phenomena and air pollution were initiated at the university's Department of Chemical Engineering. While the students graduated with a degree in chemical engineering, they nevertheless would have been trained in selected fields of environmental engineering.

Meanwhile, a diploma course in environmental engineering with options in sanitary engineering and building services engineering was available at the Ngee Ann Polytechnic to train environmental technologists for Singapore's needs. In 1985, following a request from the Ministry of the Environment to the polytechnic, a Public Health Engineering (PHE) Diploma course, which incorporated all the subjects covered by the Royal Society of Health diploma course in Environmental Health and Air Pollution Control, was offered at the polytechnic to supersede the sanitary engineering option of the environmental engineering diploma course.

Present Status

The Ngee Ann Polytechnic PHE diploma course is a three-year programme for "O" level students and is aimed at training students to become environmental technologists in the fields of water and waste water engineering, solid waste treatment and disposal, pollution control and environmental health. To date, some 200 graduates have found employment either in the government or private sectors.

At the university degree level, environmental engineering education continues to be incorporated into the existing civil engineering and chemical engineering courses. Optional courses to address emerging environmental topics (such as advanced waste treatment processes, separation technologies, environmental impact assessments and toxic and hazardous waste treatment) are regularly upgraded and offered to students. Additional postgraduate courses are also initiated whenever manpower resources are available and a sufficient number of students show interest.

Realising the significance and usefulness of a broad-based technical background to enable students to understand the new advanced topics of environmental engineering, the undergraduate subjects offered to the early years of the engineering degree courses were revamped to address the basic sciences and fundamental engineering principles. More emphasis is now placed on environmental chemistry and biochemistry. Topics on microbiology and basic chemistry of environmental pollutants are now a prerequisite before students are allowed to proceed further in the engineering degree courses.

Future Demands

The present state of affairs in environmental engineering education at the university is, however, not ideal. It is seriously hampered by the overriding need to be in balance with the wide range of courses offered to civil engineering students. While there appears to be a general appreciation of the need to place more emphasis on environmental engineering education (given the growing international momentum on environmental issues), there is a limitation on manpower resources and market opportunities for graduates in environmental engineering in Singapore. The traditional civil engineering emphasis on structures and geotechnical subjects as well as other civil engineering fields, remains important and of great significance in an urban country like Singapore. As long as environmental education in Singapore remains within the existing curricula of the civil or chemical engineering degree courses, its coverage and emphasis will be constrained and unable to keep pace with the upsurge of environmental issues that need to be addressed.

In recognition of the need to overcome this constraint, staff from the engineering and science faculties of the university have come together to consider the possibility of initiating a Diploma/MSc degree in environmental engineering. The purpose of the proposed Diploma/MSc degrees is to prepare individuals with advanced engineering capabilities in the management and control of the environment, for the protection of human health and nature's ecosystem, for conducting industrial and other human activities without adverse consequences, and for the enhancement of the quality of life. Special emphasis will be placed on developing competence in certain areas of environmental technology that have special relevance to Singapore's industrial development and manufacturing economy.

The proposed programme will be established by combining and expanding the existing educational activities concerning environmental science, environmental engineering and public health of various academic departments in the university. Basic modules that are considered necessary to courses that cover the basic science and engineering science principles upon which the practice of environmental engineering is based have been identified as:

- environmental chemistry;

- environmental microbiology;

- physical principles of environmental engineering;

- chemical and biochemical reaction engineering;

- mathematical methods for environmental engineering; and

- instrumental methods and process control.

Advanced modules are proposed to cover selected specialised fields of environmental engineering such as topics on various environmental technologies, environmental management, environmental health and environmental processes and systems.

Concluding Remarks

When the range of environmental subjects as listed above are considered, it can be seen that students intending to pursue an environmental engineering career would need to have prior education to develop the necessary fundamental skills to be able to deal with the basic, as well as the advanced, environmental topics. There appears to be a need for students to be well-versed in basic inorganic and organic chemistry, biology and life science. Perhaps the simple subject of nature study would be of relevance in addition to that of mathematics and the basic sciences. Sociology, ecosystems and economics seem to be of significance. New attitudes and capabilities are certainly needed. This AEESEAP Workshop provides a timely and excellent opportunity to consider the new attitudes and capabilities needed.

Thailand

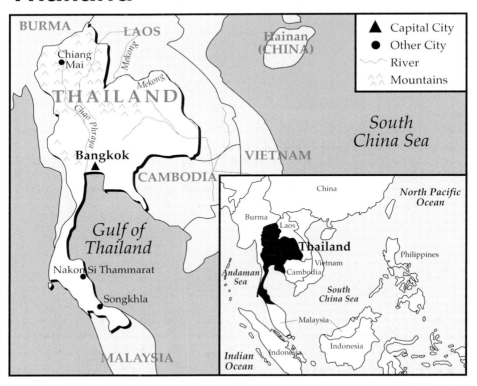

Thailand, formerly known as Siam, lies in the centre of mainland Southeast Asia and shares borders with Cambodia, Laos, Malaysia and Burma. Thailand's area is about 514,000 km^2 and the population is about 58 million. Most of the people live in villages.

There are four main regions. The north is mountainous and several rivers that run into the important Chao Phraya river originate here. The alluvial central basin of the Chao Phraya river forms the heart of Thailand. The Chao Phraya region is the most fertile due to the rich, heavy sediments deposited by the river. This region is the most heavily populated and is where Thailand's commerce, industry and farming are concentrated. Northeastern Thailand is dry and cannot support agriculture and the heavily forested Malay Peninsula contains much of the country's mineral wealth.

The climate is tropical and rainfall ranges from 140 cm a year on the lower plains of the Chao Phraya to 560 cm a year on the southeastern coast. Rice is the main crop grown, but fruits such as mangoes, bananas and pineapples are also grown. Thailand exports surplus rice and is a leading exporter of tin and rubber.

Primary school is free and compulsory for Thai children between 7 and 14 years of age. About half go on to secondary schools, vocational and teacher-training schools and higher education institutions. Thailand has several universities, including Chulalongkorn University.

Environmental Engineering Education — the Thailand Experience

Wongpun Limpaseni
Environmental Engineering Department
Chulalongkorn University
Bangkok, Thailand

Abstract

Environmental engineering education in Thailand began 40 years ago at Chulalongkorn University in Bangkok. After a slow start, the demand and recognition for environmental engineering is increasing, but has failed to keep up with economic development and the deterioration in the environment. Environmental engineering practice needs to be upgraded and the standard of practice maintained. On the other hand, the environmental engineering concept is needed in general engineering education in order to work cooperatively towards a better environment.

Introduction

In Thailand, sanitary engineers first graduated in 1954 — exactly 40 years ago. However, the sanitary engineering programme was not popular and only produced a small number of graduates. People had very little concern for the environment and the emphasis was on economic development. Master plans for sewerage systems were shelved due to lack of funds. Only in the last few years, when the environmental problem became obvious to the general public, was there a demand for action. The environmental engineering profession and education is being recognised and undergoing rapid development.

Past and Present Status

Chulalongkorn University was a pioneer in setting up an undergraduate and postgraduate programme (higher diploma and master) in sanitary engineering in 1954. However, in the early days, less than ten graduates were produced each year. It is only in the last 20 years that the programme has been producing in the range of 20 to 30 graduates each year.

Until very recently, the other two universities that graduated environmental engineers were Chiengmai University in the north and Khonkaen University in the northeast. Their total output is currently about 70 graduates per year. Environmental engineering education is being recognised. At least two more universities started programmes in 1993 and expected enrolments are almost double the existing capacity.

Programmes in environmental science and management are proliferating much more than environmental programmes in the engineering discipline. At last count, seven government universities are offering courses in environmental science and management. The combined output in the science programme is no less than 120 per year. Several private universities, as well as technical colleges, are setting up similar programmes.

Unfortunately, environmental engineering content has been found lacking in other engineering degree programmes. Among the courses that are offered by the Department of Environmental Engineering to other departments are water supply engineering, wastewater treatment and environmental impact evaluation. While some students in industrial engineering are interested in wastewater treatment, the course curriculum has not incorporated environmental engineering as an integrated part of the programme.

Demand for Environmental Engineering

Accompanying the rapid economic growth and industrialisation in Thailand is a great demand for science and technology (S & T) manpower. This is reflected in salary increases for engineers in the private sector to at least twice those in the public sector. There are only 17 S & T manpower graduates in Thailand per 10,000 population, compared to 25 in Korea and 50 in Japan ten years ago. This has prompted the government to accelerate the production of engineers.

There is a strong demand for competent environmental engineers, but where expertise is lacking, it is sometimes ignored. Pseudo-environmental engineers and below-standard work is widely accepted.

The government is investing unprecedented sums of money in the environmental programme, including wastewater treatment, solid waste disposal and air quality management. The sum, however, is still small in comparison to other developed or emerging countries. With an investment in the environmental programme of around US$2 per person per year, Thailand still has a long way to catch up with OECD countries at US$85 or Singapore at US$107. It also indicates the potential for the environmental engineering profession in Thailand.

Barriers to Environmental Engineering Development

Thailand has a singular system of registering professional engineers. Practising is restricted by law to registered engineers in the five disciplines of civil, mechanical, electrical, mining and industrial engineering. The Ministry of the Interior, through the Control of Engineering Practice Board, oversees the engineering profession for public safety and welfare. Environmental engineering is not regulated by law and the field is a "free for all".

The core group of environmental engineers has, for many years, tried to elevate the status of environmental engineering to equate with other disciplines. This is to regulate the practice in environmental engineering so that the standard is maintained and the profession is recognised. It has received little sympathy from other engineers, who fear that their "turf" will be intruded on.

Future Trends

With the passing of the new Environmental Act 1992, polluters and treatment facility operators are held responsible for their acts. With better enforcement, it is hoped to see a rise in the standard of practice that ensures proper functioning of wastewater treatment plants and the like.

With greater demand for environmental protection, there will be a need for greater cooperation from all parties concerned. For example, the waste minimisation concept will need willing cooperation from the process engineer in the factory. It necessitates basic environmental education to be included in all engineering curriculum.

The Engineering Institute of Thailand (EIT) 1994 Annual Conference theme was "Technology for Better Environment". We hope to see this as a starting point where all engineering disciplines will regard environmental engineering as an integral part of their responsibility and will use technology to bring about a better environment.

Vietnam

Vietnam lies on the eastern coast of the Indochinese peninsula and is bordered by China, Laos and Cambodia. Vietnam's 330,000 km² are home to more than 71 million people, making it one of the most densely populated countries in Southeast Asia.

Much of Vietnam is mountainous, but the coastal areas are the most populous. The Red River and Mekong River deltas contain 60 percent of the population. Most people live in small villages.

The climate is tropical and rainfall ranges from 150 cm to 200 cm annually. Vietnam is rich in natural resources such as hardwooods, iron, tin and zinc. Cash crops such as tea, coffee and spices are grown on plateaus and hill areas and rubber plantations can be found along the Cambodian border. Some of the forests and plantations were defoliated during the Vietnam War, but most are now recovering.

Despite the abundance of natural resources, Vietnam is one of Asia's poorest countries. The economy is based on agriculture, and rice is the main source of export earnings, followed by rubber. Fishing is also important and manufacturing operations are growing.

Education is free and compulsory in Vietnam, and more than 90 percent of adults are literate. Universities include the University of Hanoi, the University of Ho Chi Minh City and the Hanoi University of Civil Engineering.

The Fundamentals of Environmental Engineering Education in Vietnam

Pham Ngoc Dang — Director
Centre for Environmental Engineering
of Towns and Industrial Areas (CEETIA)
University of Hanoi

At present, there is a critical deterioration in Vietnam in the quality of water and air, and serious pollution due to noise and solid wastes in the urban centres as well as in industrial areas. Among the most affected areas are the capital city of Hanoi and Ho Chi Minh City.

Therefore, Vietnam has considerable requirements in terms of the quantity and quality of environmental engineering education.

In Vietnam, there are now about 100 universities and colleges with a total enrolment of 430,000. Included among these are 16 technical universities and colleges. Special attention has been paid to the training of environmental engineering specialists by Hanoi University of Civil Engineering, the Hanoi National University of Technology and the University of Technology of Ho Chi Minh City.

The Hanoi University of Civil Engineering has been training engineers in environmental engineering (water/waste water and solid waste engineering, air environmental technology and micro-climate engineering) since 1962. The University of Technology of Ho Chi Minh City has been training engineers in water environmental technology since 1975. The Hanoi National University of Technology has offered training in environmental engineering since 1993.

The number of trainees in the field of environmental engineering at these three universities is approximately 400, making up about 0.1% of the total number of undergraduates. The education programme meets the needs of engineers involved in the planning, design, operation and management of environmental engineering.

As formulated by the Vietnamese Ministry of Education and Training, the curricula of all technical engineering universities is of five years duration and consists of two stages.

The First Two-year Stage

The curricula at this stage are similar at all the technical engineering universities. They aim to provide students with the necessary knowledge so that after completing the course at this stage, they are able to transfer from one field of education to another within a specific university/college, or from one university/college to another at the will of the student or depending on the societal requirements of economic production.

The fundamental science subjects at this stage are mathematics, information science, physics, chemistry and mechanics.

The Second Three-year Stage

In respect to environmental engineering, this stage is divided into two sub-stages, just as environmental engineering in Vietnam is itself divided into two smaller sections — water environmental engineering and air environmental engineering. The two topics are integrated in the first one-and-a-half year course and then taught as two separate topics in a second one-and-a-half year course.

The basic subjects of environmental engineering at the second stage are:

- biological processes and technology;

- environmental chemistry;

- atmospheric climatology;

- applied microbiology;

- environmental health and sanitation;

- waste water treatment technology;

- air pollution treatment and control;

- noise pollution control;

- solid waste treatment and control; and

- environmental strategy and management.

Technology and science is changing rapidly nowadays. That is why we propose that five percent of the time in the curriculum programme should be left as free time to undertake special courses given by highly-qualified lecturers or by experienced scientists. The subjects can be changed yearly so as to keep in touch with the latest science and technology breakthroughs in environmental pollution protection engineering, both at home and abroad.

However, training in environmental engineering in Vietnam is, in general, of a lower standard compared to other countries. The main reasons for this are:

- backwardness in the curricula and methods of training;

- the lack of technical literature and teaching material; and

- the shortage of training aids, laboratory equipment and measuring devices to be used in environmental engineering.

The assistance of all our international friends is, therefore, very necessary.

Appendices

Appendix 1: Group Sessions

Engineers see themselves as facilitating the translation of humanity's dreams and visions into physical reality.

The workshop was divided into four parts:

- The Needs — What do industry and the profession require? What does an environmental engineer do? (keynote speaker: David Thom).

- Basic and Essential Requirements — What framework, attitude, skills and knowledge are required? (keynote speaker: Roger Duffell).

- Undergraduate Education — What is required during the early stages of an engineer's education? (keynote speaker: David Frost).

- Continuing Education — What are the implications for practising engineers? (keynote speaker: Sirkka Pöyry).

The keynote addresses were intended to provide direction and outline the issues for the subsequent group sessions. Following the group sessions, a final plenary session was held at which all delegates discussed issues raised in the individual sessions. An editorial team summarised the discussions and these are presented below.

Session 1 — The Needs

Who are the customers and how are engineering works initiated?

It was generally recognised that engineers serve the community and it is the community who is the ultimate recipient of engineering activity. The view was expressed that the term "stakeholder" more accurately describes the community relationship to engineering works than does the term "customer". It was concluded that whatever term is utilised, it must reflect the needs of the wider community.

Stakeholders can be divided into three categories:

Group A   those who pay (e.g. producers, operators, developers);

Group B   those who are immediately affected by engineering activities (e.g. local communities, local government, the environment);

Group C   those who may be affected in the future (e.g. the global ecosystem, its components, future generations).

Concern was voiced about the lack of a direct interface between engineers and stakeholders. There is usually direct interaction with Group A, but interaction with Groups B and C is generally through a third party.

Engineers and their clients liaise directly, but communication with communities and government tends to be indirect and the paths for feedback are much less obvious. In many cases, direct feedback only occurs when there is a failure, rather than when there is a success.

The absence of a clear and effective link between the engineer and the community has resulted in a lack of public confidence in the profession. This is particularly evident when engineering is compared with other professions, such as law, medicine and dentistry, who have much more direct contact with the community.

What does society expect of the engineer?

Does society actually see us as we see ourselves? We might aim high, but have to acknowledge a perceptional gap.

Group A people expect engineers to take account of cultural, social, economic, ethical and environmental issues in their work. However, society at large has little understanding of what professional engineers actually do, and as a consequence their expectations are unlikely to be clearly defined. There is an expectation that they will have analytical skills and to be technically competent.

Engineers see themselves as facilitating the translation of society's infrastructure needs into physical reality. However, they tend to come into the public spotlight only when there is adverse reaction to a project proposal or when there is a failure. Until greater public confidence is gained, engineers' perception of their responsibility to the environment, that of stewardship, will not be acknowledged by the wider community.

How might engineers better serve the public good?

The interested public must have access to the information upon which engineering decisions are based, and they must be able to contribute to the decision-making process. This transparency is best achieved by maintaining a code of ethics that reflects the values of society (e.g. as demonstrated through law and through engineers' perceptions as members of society and professionals expert in resource management — in its broadest sense). This would help to alleviate the disadvantages often caused by the lack of a direct interface between most stakeholders and the engineer.

It was recognised that it may not be appropriate for all information, for example commercially sensitive information, to be in the public domain.

What is the role of an environmental engineer, and is it globally consistent?

The term environmental engineer refers to *an engineer who is environmentally responsible* and all engineers should satisfy this requirement. Although the newly-developed programmes in environmental engineering emphasise this aspect of engineering education, it will be some time before these people have a major influence on the engineering ethos. Given the acknowledged urgency of the need for environmentally sensitive engineering, it is crucial that the present generation of practising engineers also recognises this need. They must learn how to integrate engineering, economics, ethics and ecology principles in their professional work.

Engineers are primarily responsible to the society in which they work and should direct their efforts towards the public good. Ultimate responsibility is to the global system, but priorities are, in many cases, derived from cultural values that are not common to all societies.

Session 2 — Aims of Environmental Engineering Education

What are the objectives of environmental education in engineering?

Engineers face increasing public challenge over the environmental and social risks associated with technological and infrastructural development. Nationally and internationally, governments are now formally committed to sustainable development. If engineers are to respond appropriately to this challenge, it is imperative that they are aware of the relevant issues and have the necessary knowledge and skills to address them.

The objectives of environmental education in the engineering context are to increase the appreciation and critical understanding of:

- the principles of sustainable development;
- the contribution engineers can make to the development of engineering for sustainability;
- the values implicit in science and engineering in relation to the social and cultural values of the wider community;
- the philosophical bases of public concern for the environment;
- the basic principles of environmental science; and
- disputes over knowledge between scientists, engineers and the public.

Engineers have skills that are crucial to the successful implementation of sustainable development. However, the above objectives have not been recognised in traditional engineering courses. As a result, engineers have generally not responded well to demands for greater public accountability and environmental sensitivity in engineering planning. Engineering education that includes the above objectives in addition to the development of more traditional knowledge and skills of the discipline result in engineers who are better equipped to serve and take a leading role in the community.

Is there a need for specialist environmental engineering programmes?

There was overwhelming support for the concept of a specialist environmental engineer. This speciality can be expected to function alongside, and to facilitate the transfer of environmental knowledge and experience to, the broader engineering profession (see Figure 1).

Interestingly, the *specialist* approach is intended to engender a *generalist* methodology, within which aspects of the broader fields of social and natural (biological and earth) sciences can be integrated. Core engineering involving cleaner production design and implementation must be seen as the essence of all engineering in the future.

Not all who claim to be "environmental engineers" are necessarily environmentally educated in the context of this workshop, i.e. recognising the significance and relevance

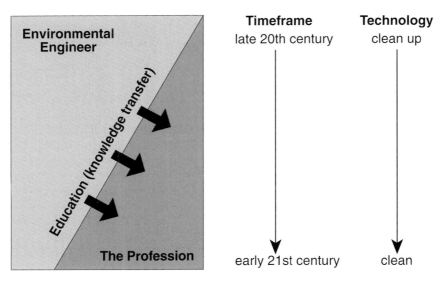

Figure 1: The relationships between technology and engineers' responsibilities in time. The role of the specialist environmental engineer will not only involve "environmental engineering", but will be to facilitate knowledge transfer to the wider engineering community, who will ultimately be expected to function as environmentally educated engineers. Although it is clear that in the early 21st century all engineers will be environmentally aware, there will be a continuing need for the specialist environmental engineer.

of pursuing sustainable management. They may simply be repackaged public health, or heating and ventilation engineers.

There are differences, both internationally and nationally, as to the form of specialist environmental engineering that should be offered at different tertiary institutions. For example, some institutions only offer postgraduate programmes. This may change as a result of client demand or changing regional and national priorities.

What is the essential knowledge of an environmental engineer?
It was recognised by those participating in the workshop that there was not a uniform representation from the different engineering disciplines. The makeup of the participants included 15 civil engineers, four chemical, three mechanical, two electrical, one mining, two geotechnical, one natural resources engineer and three scientists. Some concern was expressed about the predominance of civil engineers in the workshop and whether this could lead to a bias in the selection of "essential knowledge" in environmental engineering. It is important to recognise that although none of the participants was formally educated as a specialist "environmental engineer", 20 (64%) indicated they had been involved in environmental engineering practice, and 22 (71%) indicated that they had been involved in environmental engineering education.

Attitude was considered the key issue in the education of environmental engineers.

This *attitude* involves:

- the maintenance of an open mind and broad awareness of societal issues;

- a commitment to leadership, sustainability, ethics and quality of life for all;

- a global responsibility, including utilisation of the best knowledge currently available, in solving problems;

- an appreciation of the values inherent in people and the biosphere; and

- an acceptance of the concepts of uncertainty, complexity and change.

The *skills* needed by the environmental engineer were perceived to be:

- the ability to learn, listen and communicate;

- the development of a systems approach to thinking design and management; and

- appreciation of a balance between qualitative and quantitative assessment.

The *knowledge* base of the environmental engineer must include:

- an understanding of the contextual setting of a problem;

- an understanding of the relevant science and engineering in the context of the social, economic and ecological environment in which that knowledge is applied;

- monitoring and assessment of environmental quality and standards;

- understanding of relevant legislation and policy; and

- ethics.

These are additional to the rigorous core knowledge traditionally required for the professional engineer.

The *methodology* for transferring knowledge, skills and attitudes is ideally developed through problem-based learning and the exploration of case studies.

Session 3 — Educational Structures

How should undergraduate courses be structured to meet the above objectives?

It was generally recognised that sustainability must be an essential element of all courses in engineering and technology and its importance must be articulated clearly to students from the outset. There was agreement that sustainability must be a continuing theme throughout the entire programme.

The concept of sustainability should be explored with respect to development and growth. Management strategies which support sustainability should be investigated as should ethics and the cultural values of society. These concepts must be integrated with the technological aspects of engineering and science.

This is best achieved within a systems framework as illustrated in Figure 2.

There is a need for flexibility of approach so as to accommodate the continuing changes in the structure and expectations of society, and changes in the environment.

The idea of increasing specialisation and the desire for a common core in all engineering programmes are in direct conflict.

What are the priorities when environmental education has to be accommodated within existing course structures?

The primary aim is to gain understanding of the behaviour of real (complex) systems and how they respond to disturbances.

Programmes should place a greater emphasis on project-based learning in the later years than on conventional lectures as indicated in Figure 3.

It was stressed that projects should be based on realistic situations, and should preferably involve field work in (small) groups.

"Educating the educators" was also seen as a priority, both in and out of faculties. Academics must be convinced of the need to change, i.e. they must want to change. It may be that this is best accomplished through incentives, and top-down support is essential.

What mechanisms are required to ensure integration of the programme components?

There are two steps required:

- attitude — acceptance within engineering faculties of the need for this new approach to professional engineering education; and

- functional — the restructuring required within existing programmes to accommodate the new objectives.

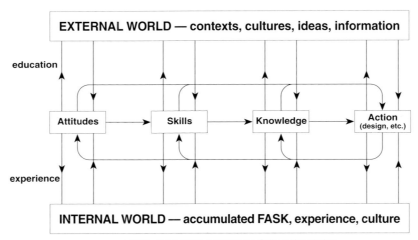

FASK = Framework + Attitudes + Skills + Knowledge

***Figure 2:** The systems framework for environmentally educating engineers.*

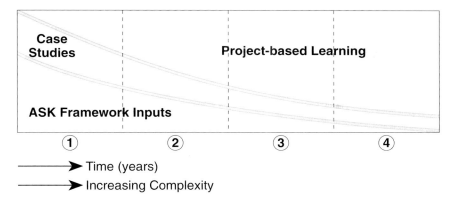

Figure 3: Core of sustainability studies (possibly equivalent to replacing design stream or, in some cases, becoming an overall course framework).

Significant attitudinal changes in the teaching of professional engineering must be driven from the top. Mechanisms available for encouraging such changes include the accreditation process (with professional involvement) and through government agencies with environmental responsibility. Agreement to the Talloires Declaration would obligate universities to address this issue.

Reinforcement of the new structure can be expected through government, industry and community interaction with educators. Involvement by a wide cross-section of the community will give common ownership and greater acceptance of the proposals. *But it will require proactive moves by environmentally sensitive engineers already in practice.*

It was noted that there is a real need for texts on mainstream engineering topics that incorporate an environmental perspective.

Session 4 — Continuing Education

Some uncertainty was voiced about the clarity of goals in sustainability-oriented continuing professional development (CPD). The reality of sustainability can only be perceived when specific cases are considered. We are all capable of recognising unsustainable practice.

What are the needs of continuing education in environmental engineering?

The aim of continuing education in environmental engineering is to upskill those practitioners who specialised in a field other than environmental engineering (i.e. most practising NZ and Australian environmental engineers) with specific knowledge in environment technologies and an appreciation of the concepts of sustainability and environmental law.

There is also a need to inculcate an environmental ethos into all branches of engineering. For existing graduates, this is best achieved through peer example in the workplace and also through continuing professional development programmes.

It was also pointed out that there are further opportunities for environmentally educating engineers if they pursue postgraduate qualifications.

Support from both practitioners and employers will only come if programmes are relevant and economically viable.

How are continuing education needs currently met?

These needs are met through postgraduate studies and continuing professional development (see Figure 4).

How should continuing education needs be met in the future?

Needs are currently being met from a provider's perspective, but not necessarily for the practitioner, where barriers such as time, cost, access, culture, politics and employers' perceptions (with respect to appropriateness) may be serious obstacles. It is necessary to "sell" the concept of environmentally-oriented continuing education in engineering through demonstration of improvements in efficiency and reductions in cost.

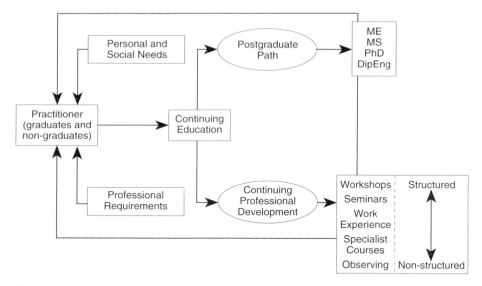

Figure 4: *Our concept of continuing education in engineering.*

Appendix 2: Workshop Participants

ARGENTINA

Mr Conrado E Bauer, President-Elect, World Federation of Engineering Organisations, Consejo Profesional de Ingenieria, Civil, Bernado de Irigoyen 330, 2°, Of. 37 (1072) Buenos Aires, ARGENTINA, +54 1 331 6398

AUSTRALIA

Assoc Prof John Brumley, Department of Civil & Geological Engineering, R M I T, GPO Box 2476V, Melbourne, Victoria 3001, AUSTRALIA, +61 3 639 0138

Dr Gary Codner, Senior Lecturer in Water Resources/Environmental Engineering, Department of Civil Engineering, Monash University, Melbourne, AUSTRALIA, +61 3 9054944

Dr John Webster, Chief Executive, Institution of Engineers Australia, 11 National Circuit, Barton ACT 2600, AUSTRALIA, +61 6 273 1488

Professor David Wilkinson, At the time of the Workshop, Professor of Civil Engineering and Director of Environmental Studies in the School of Civil Engineering, The Water Research Laboratory, University of New South Wales, King Street, Manly Vale, New South Wales 2093, AUSTRALIA. From 1 January 1995, Professor of Civil Engineering, University of Canterbury, Private Bag 4800, Christchurch, NEW ZEALAND, +64 3 364 2758

Mr Harry Wragge, Chairman, Accreditation Board, Institution of Engineers, Australia, 11 National Circuit, Barton ACT 2600, AUSTRALIA, +61 6 273 1488

BRUNEI DARUSSALAM

Dr Mirhassan Abu Bakar, Director, Institut Teknologi Brunei, Jalan Muara, PO Box 2909, Bandar Seri Begawan 1929, BRUNEI DARUSSALAM, +673 2 330776

CHINA

Professor Jiang Zhanpeng, Dept of Environmental Engineering, Tsinghua University, Beijing 100084, CHINA, +861 2562768

FINLAND

Ms Sirkka Poyry, Director, The Finnish Association of Graduate Engineers TEK, Ratavartijankatu 2, FIN - 00520, Helsinki, FINLAND, +358 0 1590306

HONG KONG

Dr Mark Davidson, Department of Civil and Structural Engineering, Hong Kong University of Science and Technology, Clear Water Bay, Kowloon, HONG KONG, +852 358 1534

INDONESIA

Dr Asis Djajadiningrat, Institution of Engineers Indonesia, Polman-ITB, Tromol Pos 851, Bandung 40008, INDONESIA, +62 22 2506605

JAPAN

Professor Naomasa Nakajima, Director of R.A.C.E., C/- Mechanical Engineering Dept, Engineering Faculty, University of Tokyo, 7-3-1, Hongo, Bunkyo-ku, Tokyo 112, JAPAN, +81 3 3815 8356

Professor Norihito Tambo, Dean of Faculty of Engineering, Professor of Sanitary & Environmental Engineering, Hokkaido University, North 13 West 8, Kita-ku, Sapporo 060, JAPAN, +81 11 707 2911

MALAYSIA

Professor Mohd. Ali Hashim, Dean, Institute for Advanced Studies, University of Malaya, 59100 Kuala Lumpur, MALAYSIA, +60 3 756 8940

NEW ZEALAND

Mr John Blakeley, Executive Director, Centre for Advanced Engineering, University of Canterbury, Private Bag 4800, Christchurch, NEW ZEALAND, +64 3 364 2069

Dr Roger Blakeley, Secretary for the Environment, Ministry for the Environment, PO Box 10362, Wellington, NEW ZEALAND, +64 4 471 0195

Dr AJ (Tony) Bowen, Secretary-General, AEESEAP, Department of Mechanical Engineering, University of Canterbury, Private Bag 4800, Christchurch, NEW ZEALAND, +64 3 364 2078

Dr John Buckeridge, Head of Civil and Environmental Engineering, UNITEC Institute of Technology, Private Bag 92025, Auckland, NEW ZEALAND, +64 9 815 4326

Dr Tim Davies, Reader, Department of Natural Resources Engineering, PO Box 84, Lincoln University, Canterbury, NEW ZEALAND, +64 3 325 3845

Professor David Elms, President of AEESEAP, Department of Civil Engineering, University of Canterbury, Private Bag 4800, Christchurch, NEW ZEALAND, +64 3 364 2758

Mr Ian Gunn, Senior Lecturer, Department of Civil and Resource Engineering, University of Auckland, Private Bag 92019, Auckland, NEW ZEALAND +64 9 373 7462

Associate Professor John Hay, Environmental Science, Faculty of Science, The University of Auckland, Private Bag 92019, Auckland, NEW ZEALAND +64 9 373 7470

Mr Bob Hill, Chairman, IPENZ Engineering and Environment Committee, Carter Holt Harvey Ltd, Private Bag 92106, Auckland, NEW ZEALAND, +64 9 262 6197

Dr Mark Milke, Lecturer, Department of Civil Engineering, University of Canterbury, Private Bag 4800, Christchurch, NEW ZEALAND, +64 3 364 2758

Mr Armour Mitchell, Chief Executive, IPENZ, PO Box 12-241, Wellington, NEW ZEALAND, +64 4 473 2324

Ms Leigh Newport, Department of Civil Engineering, University of Canterbury, Private Bag 4800, Christchurch, NEW ZEALAND, +64 3 364 2758

Dr John Peet, Senior Lecturer, Department of Chemical and Process Engineering, University of Canterbury, Private Bag 4800, Christchurch, NEW ZEALAND, +64 3 364 2063

Mr David Thom, President, WFEO Committee on Engineering, and Environment, C/- Kingston Morrison Ltd, PO Box 9806, Auckland, NEW ZEALAND, +64 9 520 4695

Ms Anna Walls, Department of Civil Engineering, University of Canterbury, Private Bag 4800, Christchurch, NEW ZEALAND, +64 3 364 2758

PAPUA NEW GUINEA

Dr Nimal Subasinghe, Senior Lecturer, Mineral Process Engineering, Dept of Mining Engineering, Papua New Guinea University of Technology, Private Mail Bag, Lae, PAPUA NEW GUINEA, +675 45 7534

PHILIPPINES

Professor Marino M Mena, College of Engineering, University of the Philippines, Diliman, Quezon City 1101, PHILIPPINES, +63 2 922 47 14, +632 993144

SINGAPORE

Dr Lawrence C C Koe, Assoc Prof & Chartered Engineer, Department of Civil Engineering, National University of Singapore, 10 Kent Ridge Crescent, SINGAPORE 0511, +65 779 1635

THAILAND

Professor Wongpun Limpaseni, Chairman, EIT Environmental Engineering Committee, Environmental Engineering Dept, Chulalongkon University, Phayathai Rd, Bangkok 10330, THAILAND, +66 2 2186680

UNITED KINGDOM

Professor Roger Duffell, Department of Civil Engineering, University of Hertfordshire, Hatfield Campus, College Lane, Hatfield, Herts, AL10 9AB, ENGLAND, +44 707 284126

UNITED STATES OF AMERICA

Dr David Frost, Associate Professor, School of Civil Engineering, Georgia Institute of Technology, Atlanta, Georgia 30332, USA, +1 404 894 2278

VIETNAM

Professor Dr Pham Ngoc Dang, Director of Centre for Environmental Engineering of Towns and Industrial Areas, Civil Engineering, University of Hanoi, 5 Giai Phong Boulevard, Hanoi, VIETNAM, +84 4 691 684

Appendix 3: Biographies

Special Invited Guest

Mr Conrado E Bauer
President-Elect
World Federation of Engineering Organisations
Consejo Professional de Ingenieria Civil
Bernado de Irigoyen 330
2° Of. 37
(1072) Buenos Aires
ARGENTINA

Conrado Ernesto Bauer was born in La Plata city, Argentina, in 1927. He is a Civil Engineer, graduating from the University of La Plata. He carried out postgraduate courses in Argentina, Spain and USA. He has been professor and dean of the Faculty of Physics and Mathematics and Vice-president of the National University of La Plata.

He performed professional and business activities (dwellings, design of resistant structures and road works and building constructions) and was, until 1993, President of ECOTEC Consultants, a society founded in 1970 devoted to economic and engineering studies and advising. Between 1958 and 1983 he worked in the public administration as Undersecretary of Public Works of the Municipality of La Plata, Undersecretary and Minister of Public Works of the Buenos Aires province, Minister of social Welfare and Minister of Works and Public services of Argentina.

As regards engineering organisations, he was Vice-president of the Centre of Engineers of the Buenos Aires province, President of the committees of Engineering and Environment of the UADI (Argentine Union of Engineering Associations) and of the WFEO (1979-1987). Currently he is President of the Environment and Sustainable Development Commission of the Argentine Centre of Engineers, President of the International Relations Committee of UADI, and President-elect of WFEO, where he chairs the Engineering Affairs committee.

In addition, he is currently a member of the Engineering Academy (Buenos Aires province), technical consultant and president, director or adviser of national and international institutions and foundations.

Workshop Convenor

Professor David G Elms
President AEESEAP
Department of Civil Engineering
University of Canterbury
Private Bag 4800
Christchurch
NEW ZEALAND

David Elms has a BA from Cambridge University and a PhD from Princeton. He worked as a structural engineer with the De Havilland Aircraft Company at Hatfield, England for three years before moving to America and, eventually, to New Zealand where he joined the Civil Engineering Department at the University of Canterbury in 1964. He has been Professor of Civil Engineering since 1977. He is a Fellow of the Institution of Professional Engineers, New Zealand, and is currently President of the Association for Engineering Education of Southeast Asia and the Pacific. His principal research interests are in risk assessment and the behaviour of complex engineering systems, with the latter leading naturally to a general interest in philosophical and methodological issues in engineering. Other interests are environmental issues and geomechanics. He is an active consultant in the area of risk assessment and risk management. He is the author of more than 100 publications, and the joint author, with Sir Edward Somers and Professors Patricia Bergquist and Alan Poletti, of *The Safety of Nuclear Powered Ships* (1992).

Keynote Speakers

Dr Roger W G Blakeley
Secretary for the Environment
Ministry for the Environment
PO Box 10362
Wellington
NEW ZEALAND

Roger Blakeley completed a BE (Hons) degree in 1967 and then undertook research for his PhD in structural and earthquake engineering, also at the University of Canterbury. After ten years working on structural design and special projects for the Ministry of Works he obtained a Harkness Fellowship and studied at Stanford University for a MS degree under the Sloan Management Programme.

After returning to New Zealand in 1982 he held senior management positions within the Ministry of Works and State Coal before being appointed as the first permanent head at the Ministry of the Environment in 1987. In this position he had a key role in the promotion and development of the Resource Management Act which became law in New Zealand in 1991.

Roger is a Past Chairman of the OECD Environment Committee.

Mr David A Thom
President
WFEO Committee on Engineering and Environment
c/o Kingston Morrison Ltd
PO Box 9806
Auckland
NEW ZEALAND

David Thom retired about five years ago after a long and distinguished career in consulting engineering with the firm of Kingston Reynolds Thom and Allerdice Ltd which became KRTA Ltd (and more recently Kingston Morrison). David was President of the Institution of Professional Engineers New Zealand in 1979/80.

In addition to his present important role with WFEO, David is currently Chairman of the FEISEAP Standing Committee on Engineering and Environment, a member of the board of engineering Education and Training of the Commonwealth Engineers council.

He is also a member of the Board of Studies for Environmental Studies at the University of Auckland, a member of its School of Engineering Faculty Advisory Committee on Environmental Education and a member of the Environmental Management Advisory Committee for its Tamaki Campus.

David is also the New Zealand Qualifications Authority External Monitor for the new B.Tech (environmental) degree of UNITEC — Institute of Technology in Auckland.

David has been awarded the CBE and has had a long association with the National Parks in New Zealand.

Professor Roger Duffell
Department of Civil Engineering
University of Hertfordshire
Hatfield Campus
College Lane
Hatfield, Herts, AL10 9AB
ENGLAND

Roger Duffell is currently Professor and Director of Studies in Civil Engineering, University of Hertfordshire, United Kingdom. He was educated at Loughborough Grammar School, Leicester and Nottingham Polytechnics and Birmingham University. Completing his doctorate in 1982 he has held his current position since 1987. Roger was responsible for academic developments in civil and building services engineering, construction and surveying. He has promoted many short courses and symposia in highways and transportation and 14 courses with the Field Studies Council on environmental conservation and engineering. He is engaged in highway maintenance research sponsored by the Science and Engineering Research Council (SERC) and local authorities. He is on the ICE Council and is the UK representative of the WFEO Environmental Committee.

Dr Gary Codner
Department of Civil Engineering
Monash University
Clayton
Victoria 3168
AUSTRALIA

Gary Codner is a Senior Lecturer in Water Resources/Environmental Engineering and Convener of the Committee of Monash University which recently developed an environmental engineering degree programme due to commence in 1995. He has recently written several papers on environmental engineering education.

Gary is currently Chairman of the National Committee on Environmental Engineering for the Institution of Engineers Australia and has been involved in the development of the Institution's policy on Sustainability and Environmental Principles for Engineers. He is also a member of the Institution's Task Force on Sustainable Development.

Dr David Frost
Associate Professor
School of Civil Engineering
Georgia Institute of Technology
Atlanta
Georgia 30332
USA

David Frost is an Associate Professor and coordinator of the Geotechnical/Geo-environmental Program in the School of Civil and Environmental Engineering at the Georgia Institute of Technology. He holds Bachelors degrees in Mathematics and Civil Engineering from Trinity College, Dublin, Ireland. After working in Canada for the geotechnical consulting firm of Golder Associates, he obtained Masters and Doctoral degrees from Purdue University, Indiana, USA. He was an Assistant Professor at Purdue University, before joining Georgia Tech to lead the development of the geo-environmental program. The focus of much of his teaching and research work is integrating computer-based technologies such as geographic information systems, digital image processing and artificial intelligence in developing solutions to subsurface environmental problems.

Ms Sirkka Poyry
Director
The Finnish Association of Graduate Engineers TEK
Ratavartijankatu 2
FIN - 00520, Helsinki
FINLAND

Sirkka Poyry is Director of the Finnish Association of Graduate Engineers TEK.

She is also a council Member of the International Association of continuing Engineering Education (IACEE) and a Council Member of the European Society for Engineering (SEFI) and Chairman of the SEFI Working Group on Women in Engineering and Vice-Chairman of the SEFI Working Group on Environmental Engineering.

Sirkka is also Co-ordinator of the COMETT II VETP-EEE, University-Enterprise Training Partnership in Environmental Engineering Education.

CENTRE FOR ADVANCED ENGINEERING

The Centre for Advanced Engineering was founded in May 1987 to mark the centenary of the School of Engineering at the University of Canterbury.

The objective of the Centre is to enhance engineering knowledge within New Zealand in identified areas judged to be of national importance and to engage in technology transfer of the latest research information available from overseas. The Centre is not concerned with basic engineering research, but with the application of research findings to engineering problems.

The Centre undertakes major projects, bringing together a selected group of practising and research engineers and experts in the particular field from both New Zealand and overseas to:

- consolidate existing knowledge
- study advanced techniques
- develop approaches to particular problems in engineering and technology
- promote excellence in engineering
- disseminate findings through documentation and public seminars.

A unique forum for co-operation among industry, the engineering profession and university research engineers is thus provided.

The Centre also carries out smaller projects on engineering subjects of current concern, and arranges lectures and seminars on appropriate topics as the occasion arises.

For further information on the Centre's activities and publications, contact:

Centre for Advanced Engineering
University of Canterbury
Private Bag 4800
Christchurch, New Zealand
Telephone: +64 3 364 2478
Facsimile: +64 3 364 2069
e-mail: j.blakeley@cae.canterbury.ac.nz

Executive Director: John P Blakeley
Projects Director: John L Lumsden